THE BEATLES

GUITAR TAB EDITION

D1586314

Wise Publications
London / New York / Paris / Sydney / Copenhagen / Berlin / Madrid / Hong Kong / Tokyo

Published by
Wise Publications
14-15 Berners Street, London W1T 3LJ, UK.

Exclusive Distributors:
Music Sales Limited
Distribution Centre, Newmarket Road,
Bury St Edmunds, Suffolk IP33 3YB, UK.
Music Sales Pty Limited
20 Resolution Drive, Caringbah, NSW 2229, Australia.

Order No. NO90750
ISBN 0-7119-8798-X

Printed in the EU.

LOVE ME DO

Words & Music by John Lennon & Paul McCartney

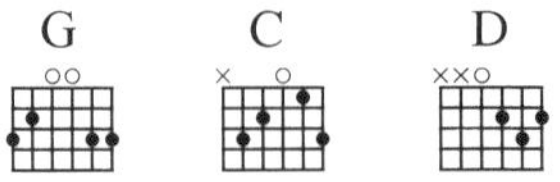

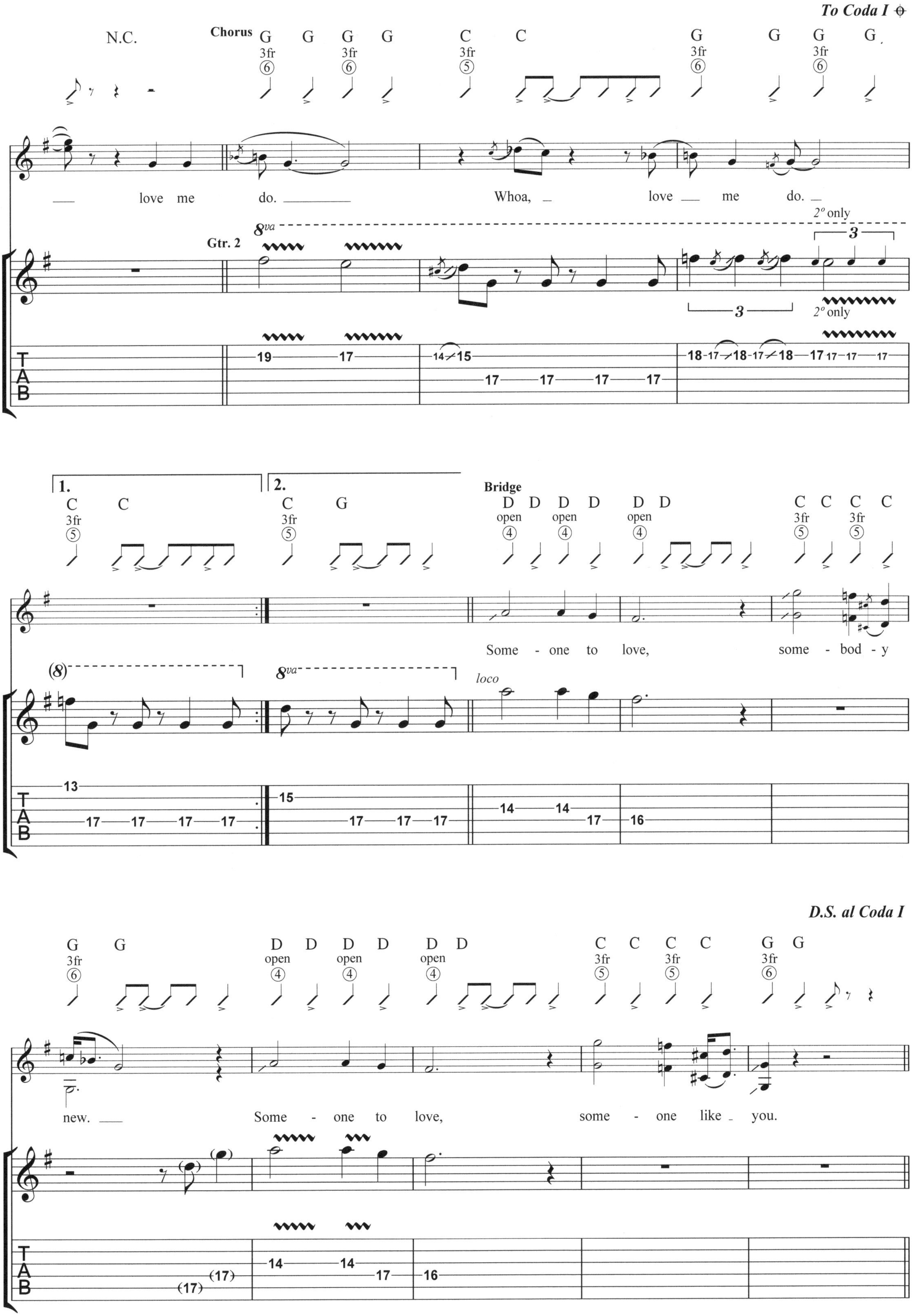
To Coda I
N.C.
Chorus
G G G G C C G G G G
3fr 3fr 3fr 3fr 3fr
love me do.
Whoa, love me do.
8va
Gtr. 2
2º only
1.
2.
C C C G
Bridge
D D D D D D C C C C
open open open 3fr 3fr
Some - one to love, some - bod - y
(8)
8va
loco
D.S. al Coda I
G G D D D D D D C C C C G G
3fr open open open 3fr 3fr 3fr
new. Some - one to love, some - one like you.

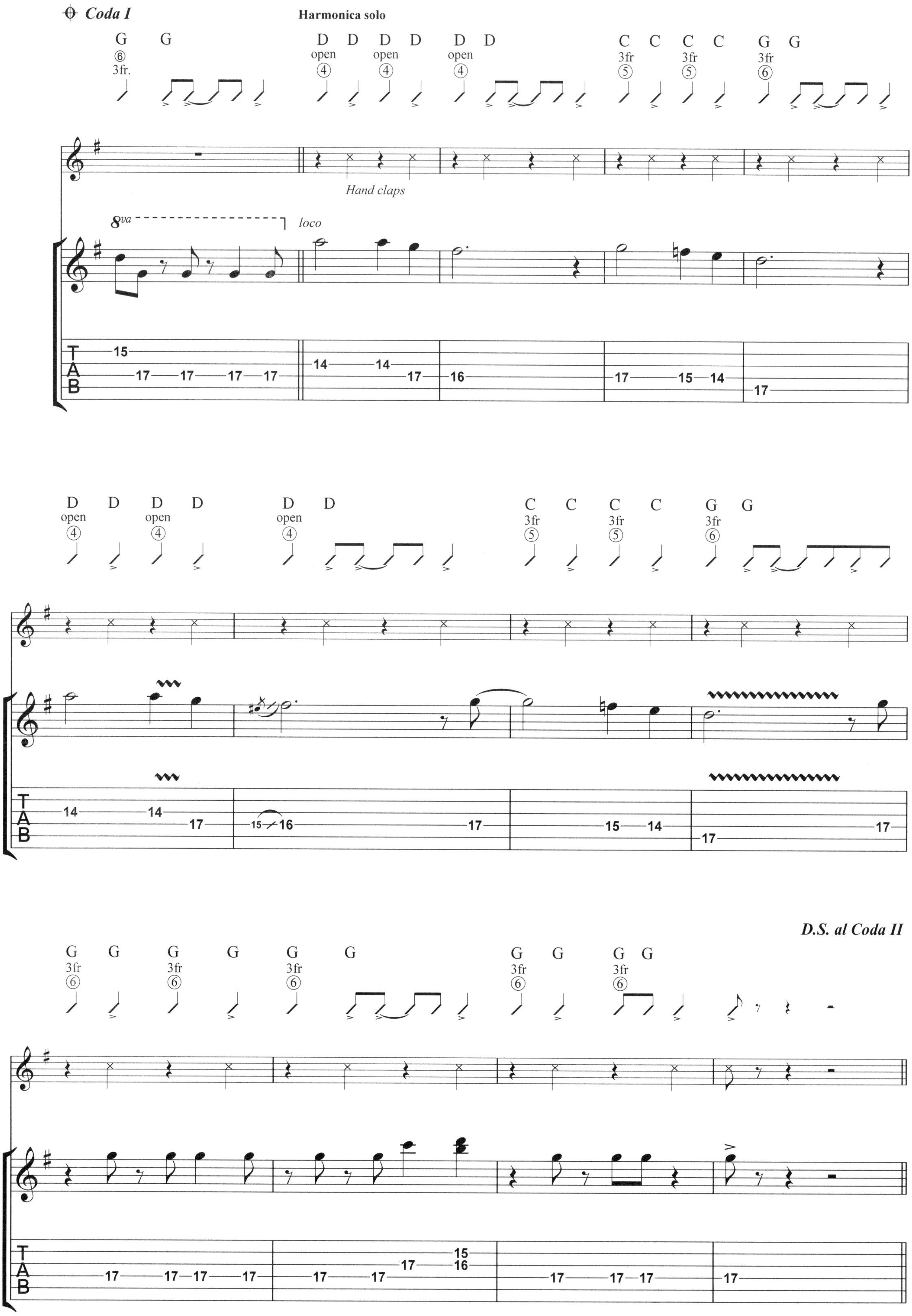
Coda I
Harmonica solo
G G D D D D D D C C C C G G
open open open
3fr 3fr 3fr
Hand claps
8va
loco
D D D D D D C C C C G G
open open open
3fr 3fr 3fr
D.S. al Coda II
G G G G G G G G G G
3fr 3fr 3fr 3fr 3fr

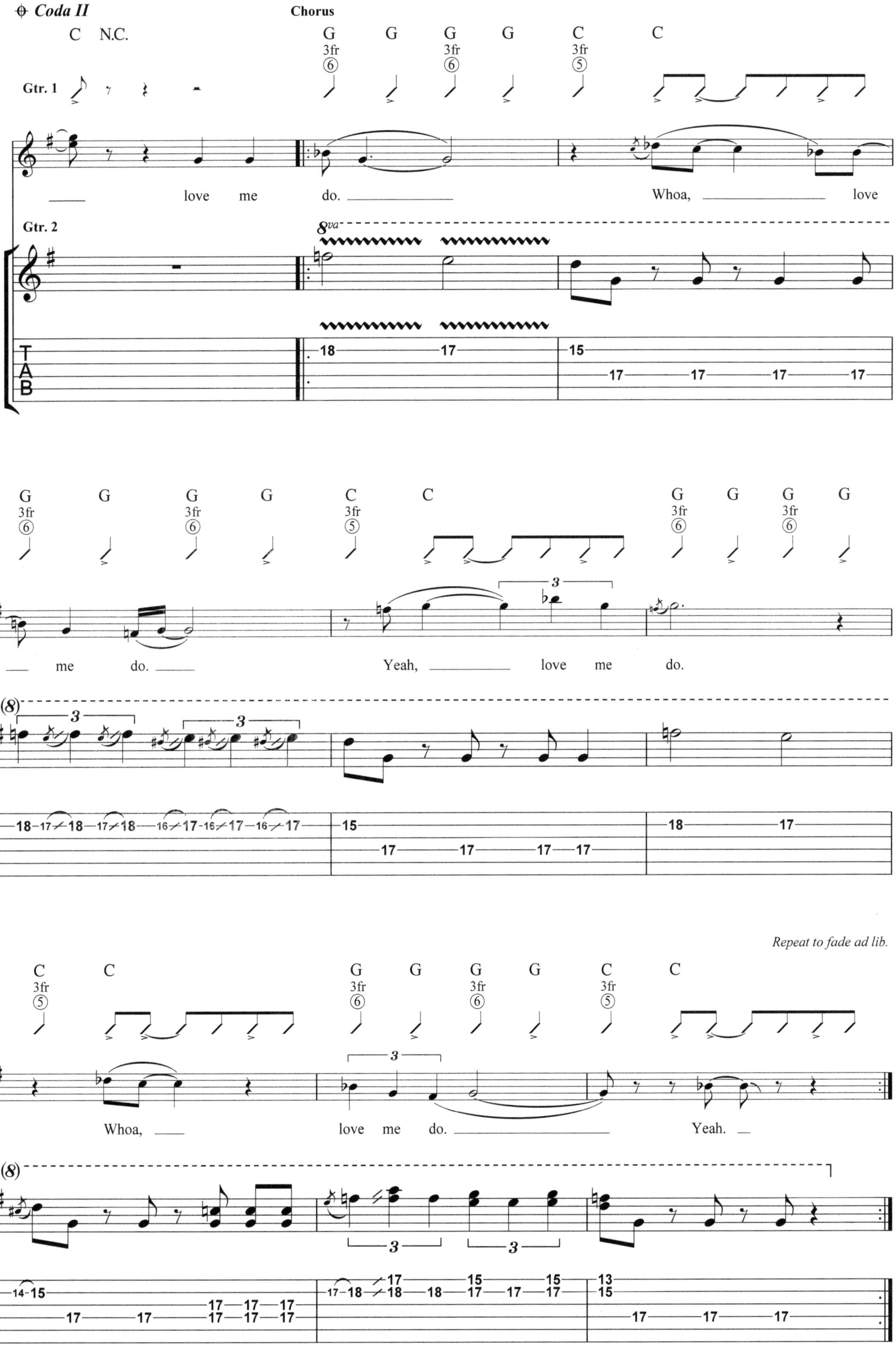
Coda II
Chorus
C N.C.
G G G G C C
Gtr. 1
love me do.
Whoa, love
Gtr. 2
me do.
Yeah, love me do.
Repeat to fade ad lib.
Whoa,
love me do.
Yeah.

FROM ME TO YOU

Words & Music by John Lennon & Paul McCartney

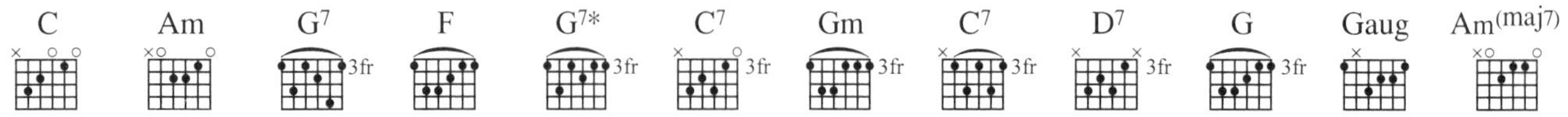

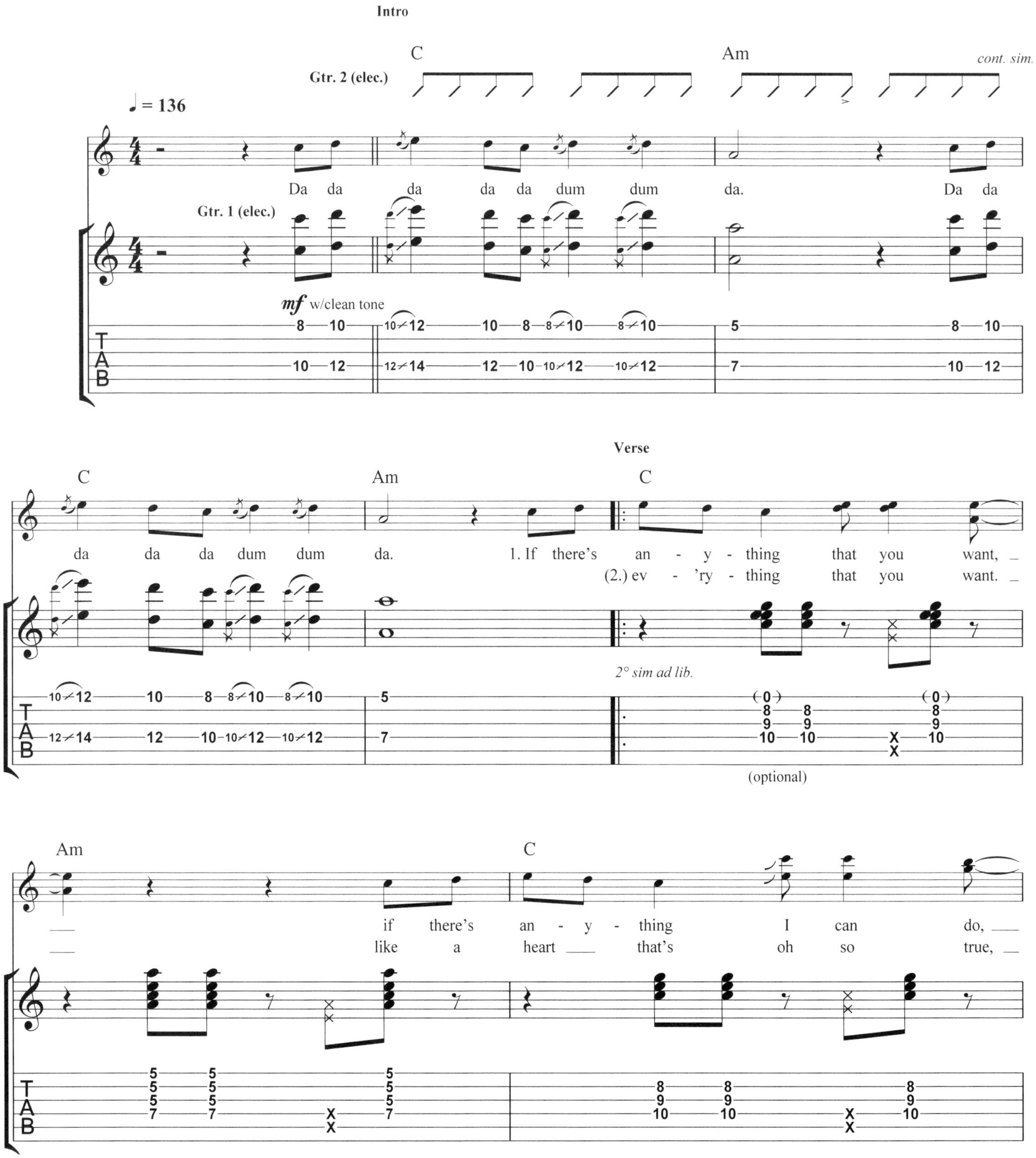

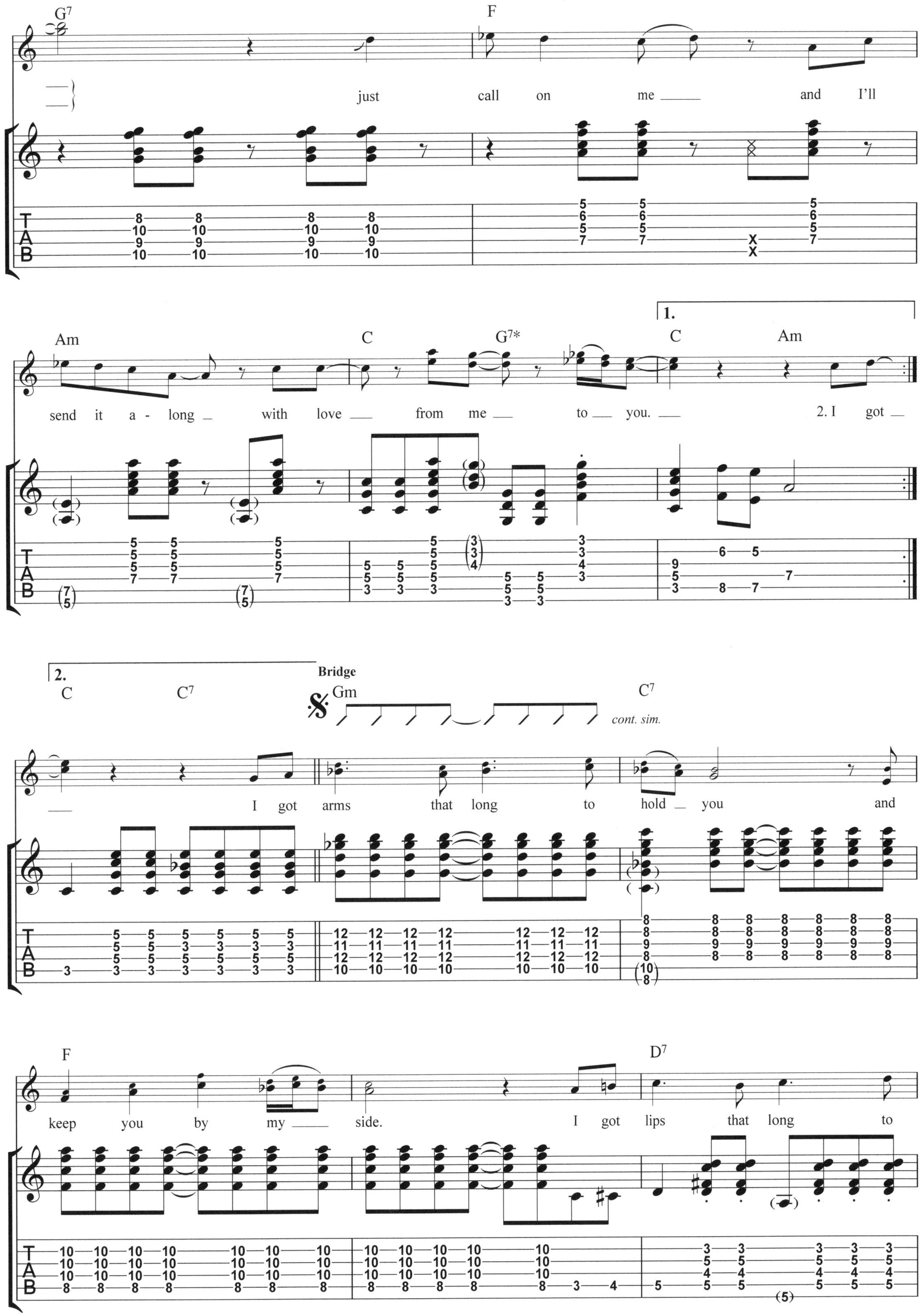
G7
F
just call on me and I'll
Am
C
G7*
1.
C
Am
send it a - long with love from me to you. 2. I got
2.
C
C7
Bridge
Gm
C7
cont. sim.
I got arms that long to hold you and
F
D7
keep you by my side. I got lips that long to
T
A
B

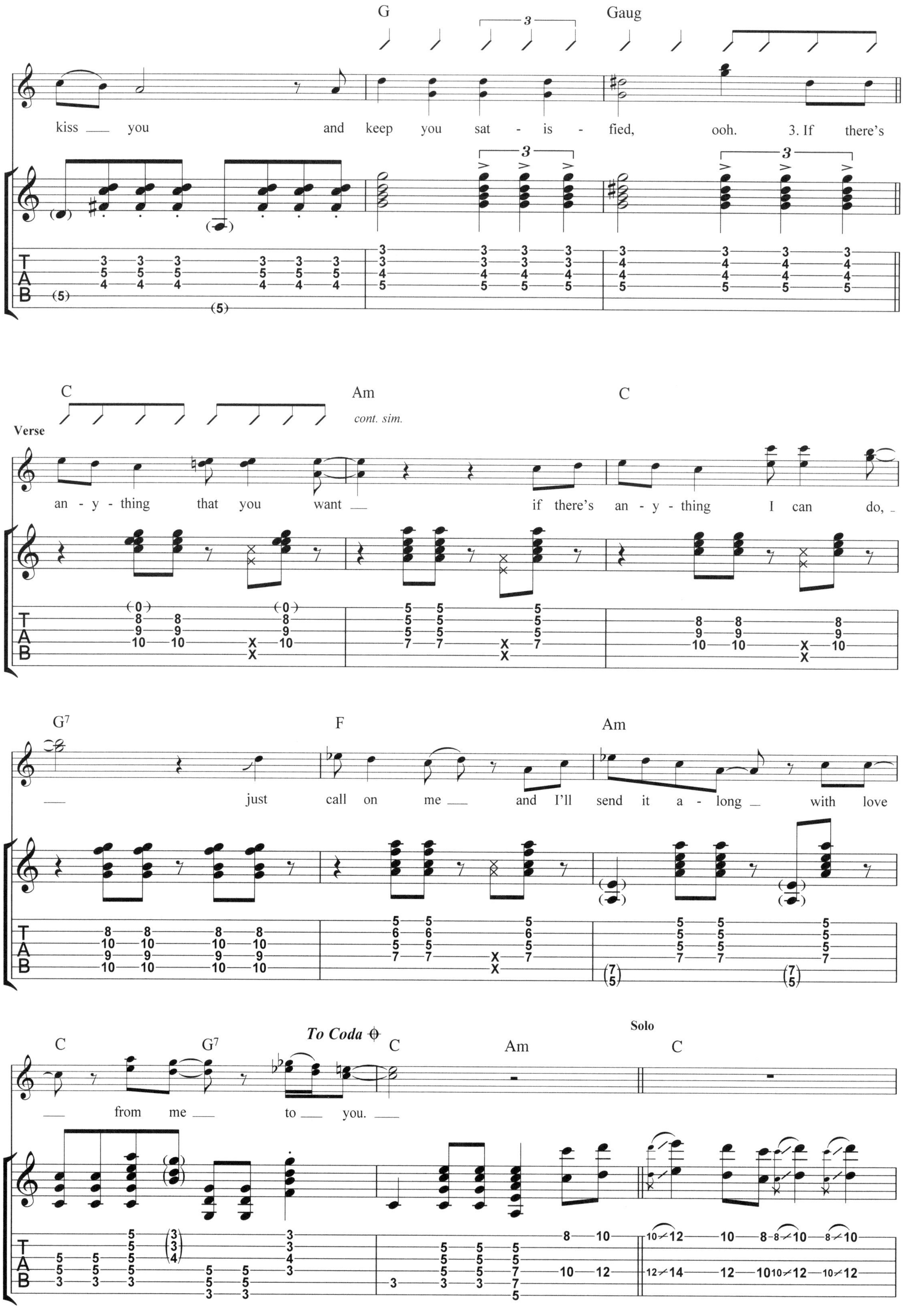
G Gaug
kiss you and keep you sat - is - fied, ooh. 3. If there's
Verse
C Am C
cont. sim.
an - y - thing that you want if there's an - y - thing I can do,
G7 F Am
just call on me and I'll send it a - long with love
C G7 To Coda C Am Solo C
from me to you.
TAB

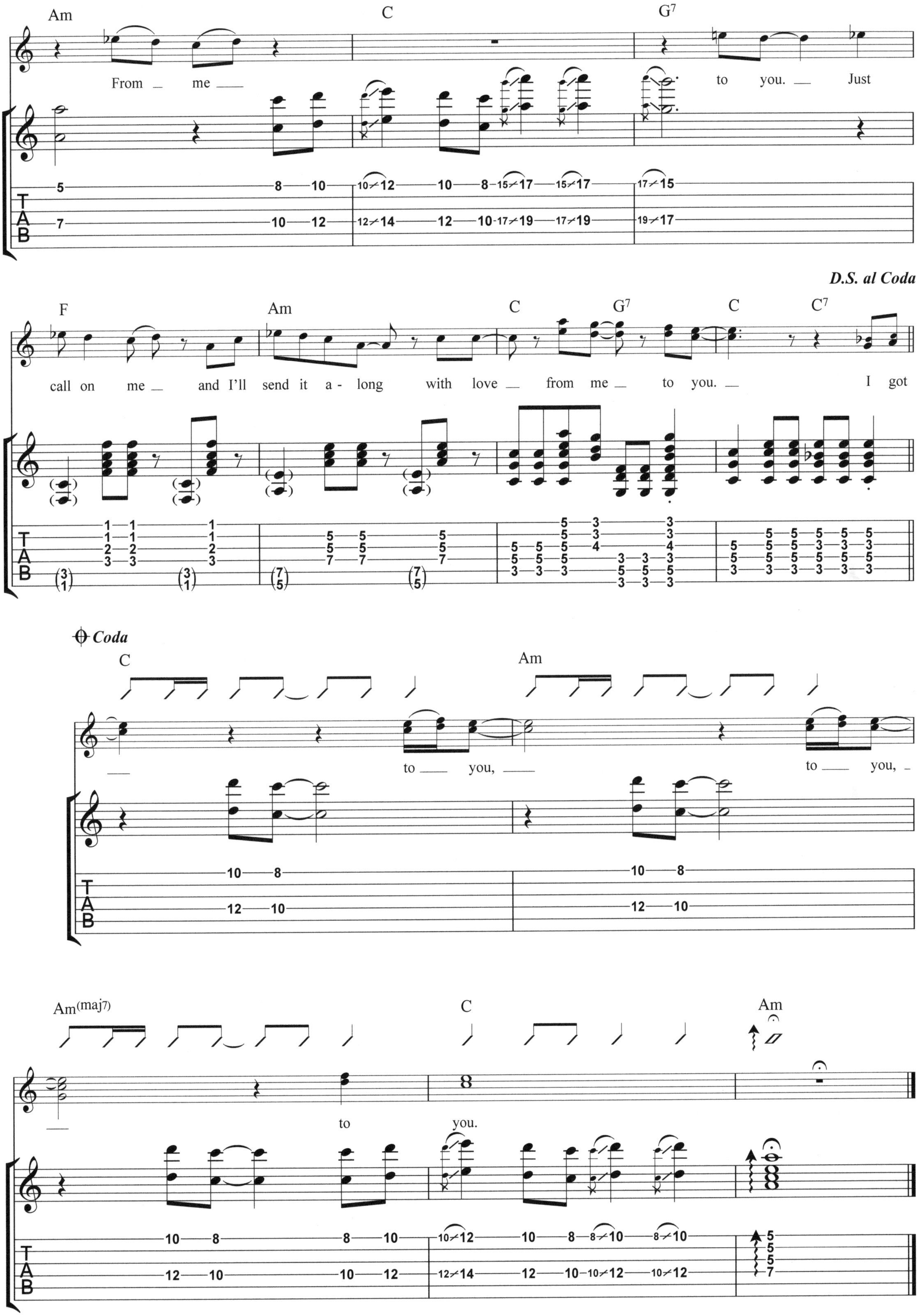
Am
C
G7
From me to you. Just
D.S. al Coda
F
Am
C
G7
C
C7
call on me and I'll send it a - long with love from me to you. I got
Coda
C
Am
to you, to you,
Am(maj7)
C
Am
to you.

SHE LOVES YOU

Words & Music by John Lennon & Paul McCartney

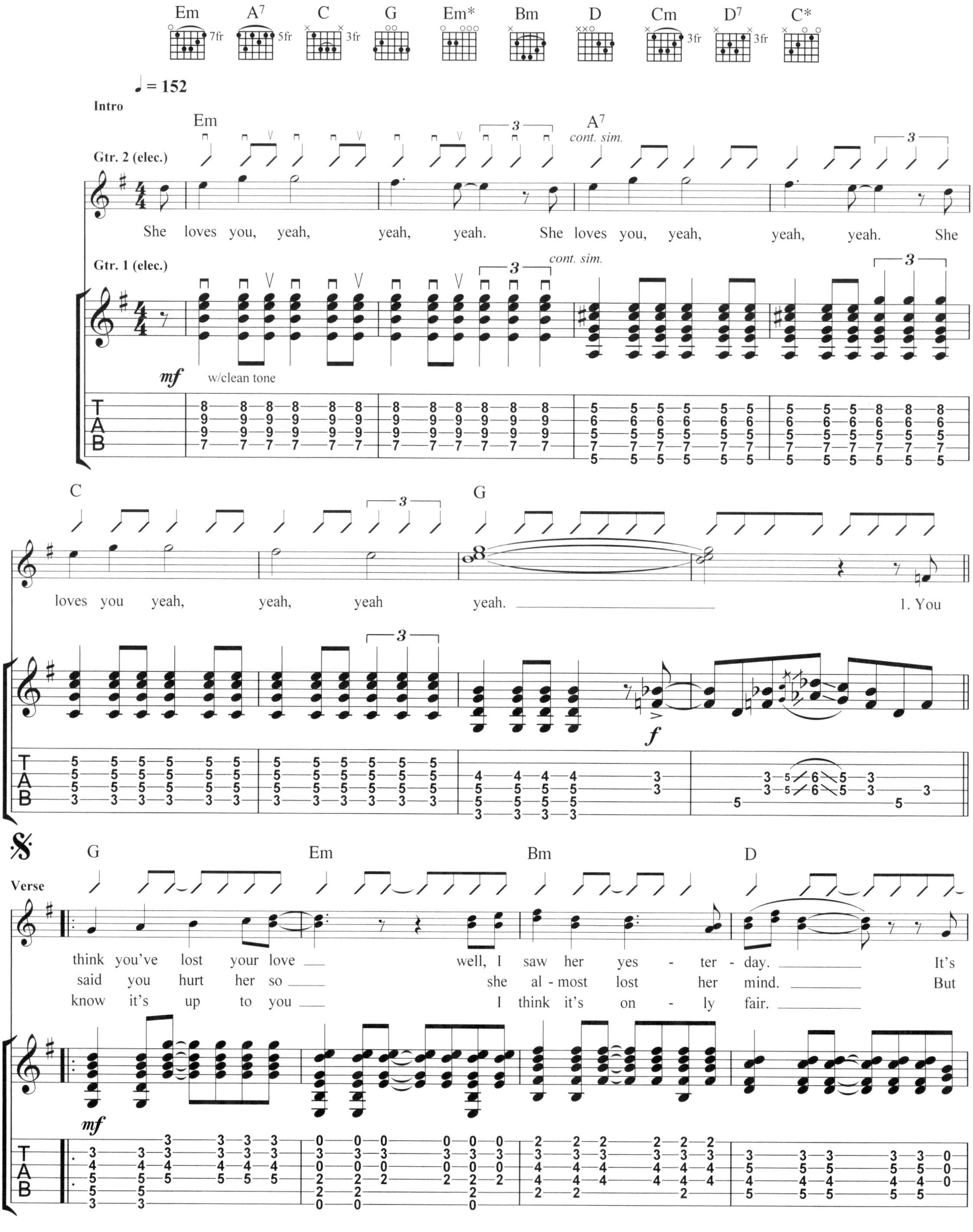

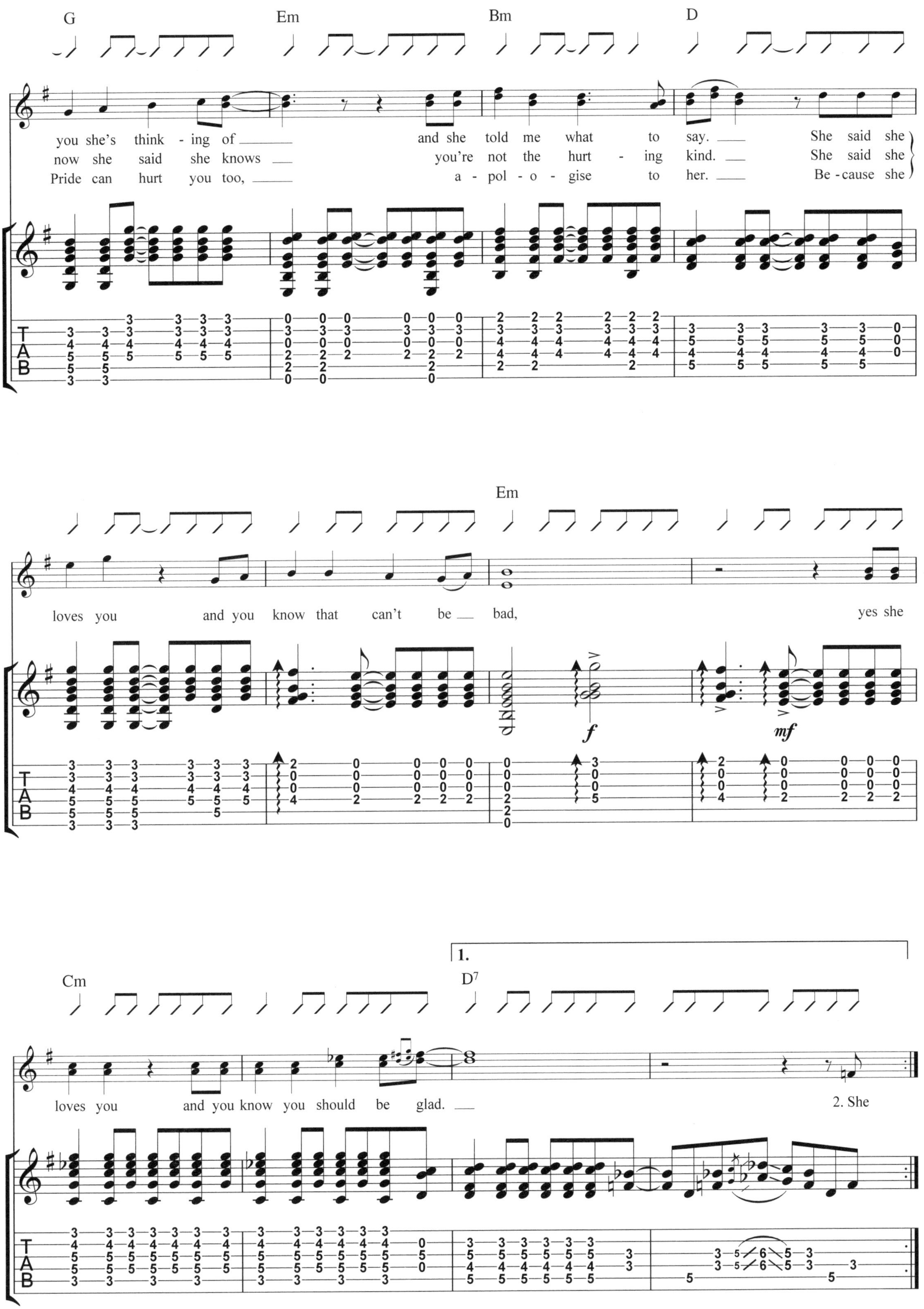
G
Em
Bm
D
you she's thinking - ing of and she told me what to say. She said she
now she said she knows you're not the hurt - ing kind. She said she
Pride can hurt you too, a - pol - o - gise to her. Be - cause she
Em
loves you and you know that can't be bad, yes she
Cm
1.
D7
loves you and you know you should be glad.
2. She
f
mf

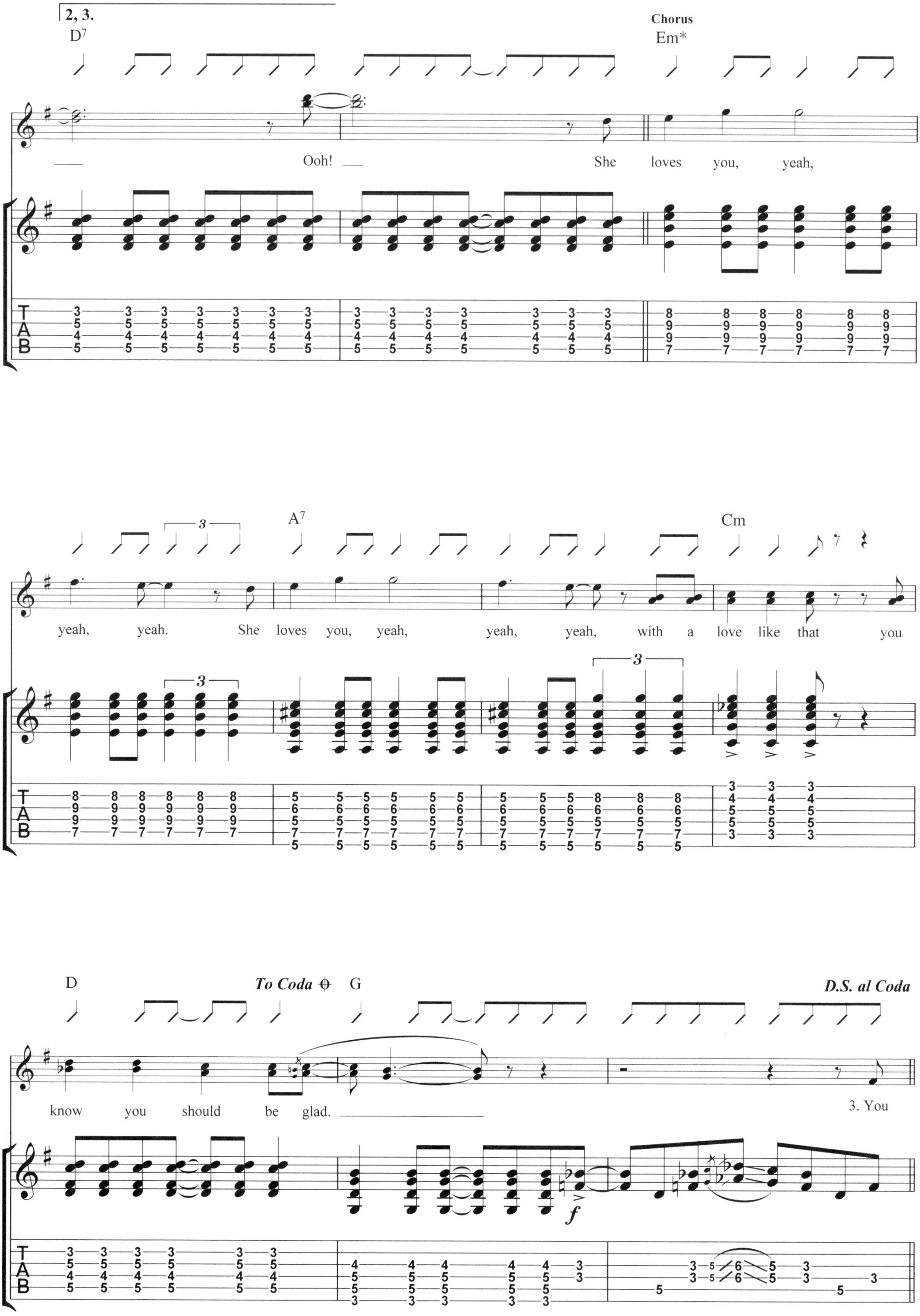
2, 3.
D7
Chorus
Em*
Ooh!
She loves you, yeah,
A7
Cm
yeah, yeah. She loves you, yeah, yeah, yeah, with a love like that you
D
To Coda
G
D.S. al Coda
know you should be glad.
3. You

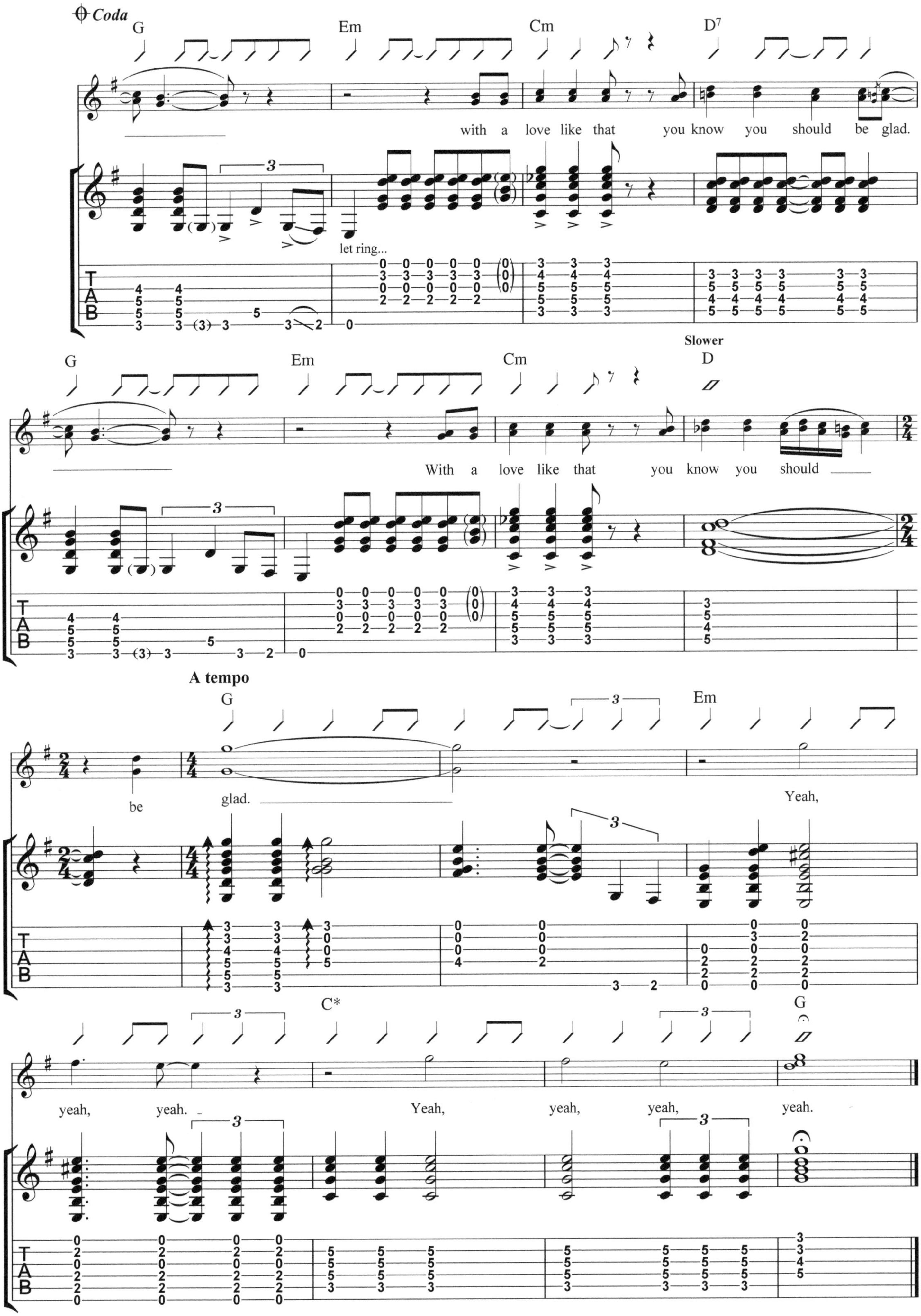
Coda
G Em Cm D7
with a love like that you know you should be glad.
let ring...
G Em Cm
Slower
D
With a love like that you know you should
A tempo
G Em
be glad.
Yeah,
C*
G
yeah, yeah.
Yeah, yeah, yeah, yeah.

I WANT TO HOLD YOUR HAND

Words & Music by John Lennon & Paul McCartney

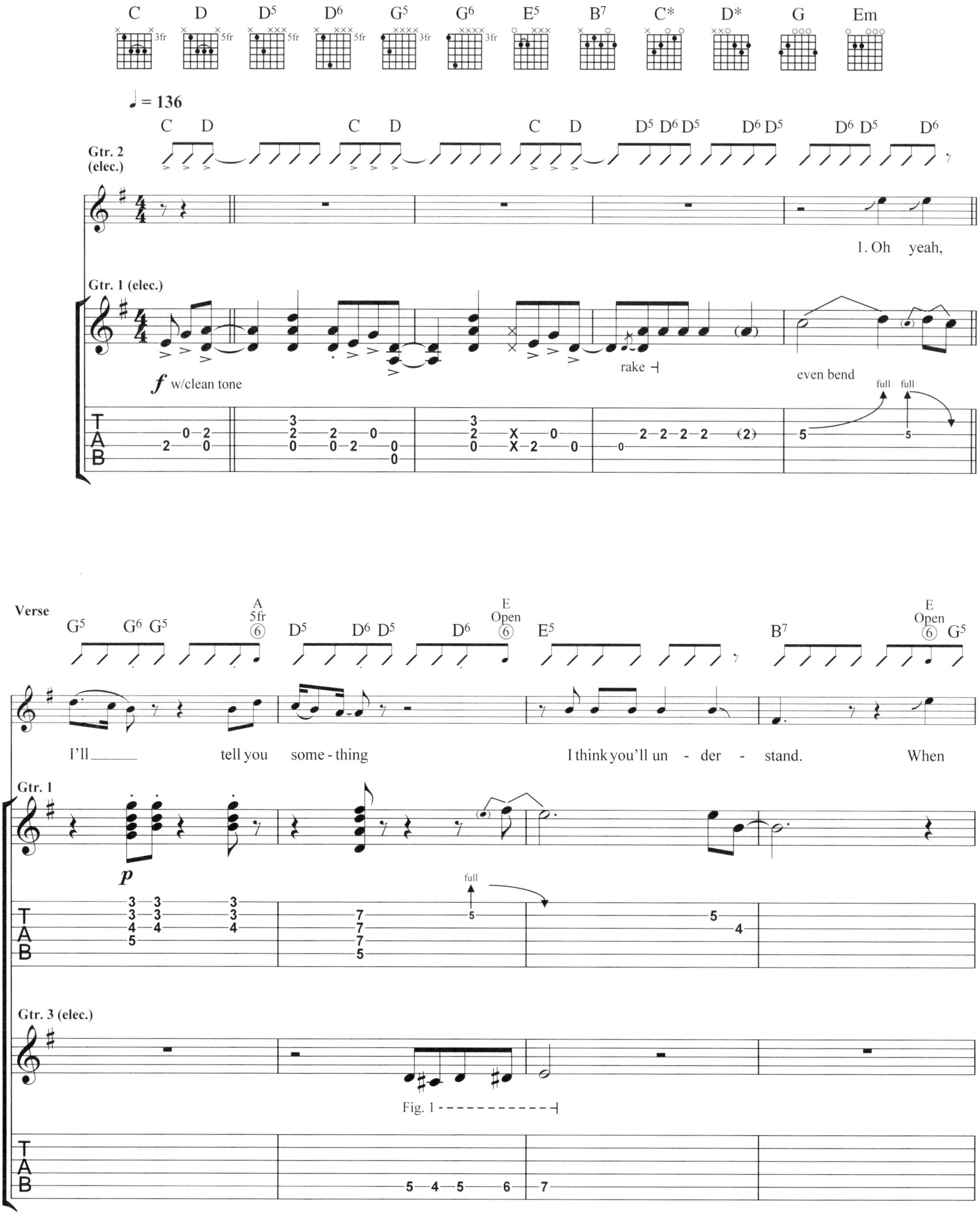

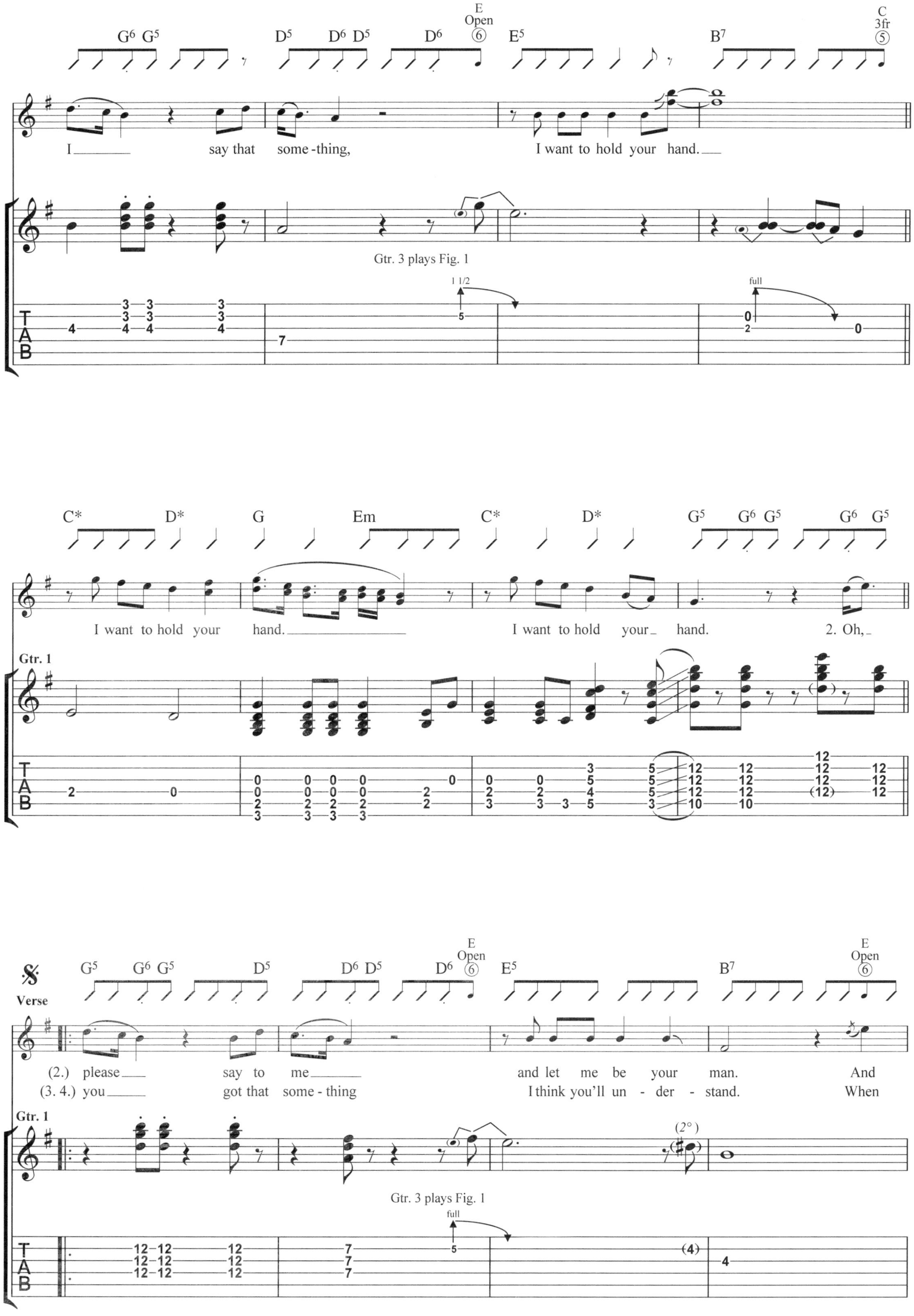
G6 G5 D5 D6 D5 D6 E Open 6 E5 B7 C 3fr 5
I say that some-thing, I want to hold your hand.
Gtr. 3 plays Fig. 1
1 1/2
full
C* D* G Em C* D* G5 G6 G5 G6 G5
I want to hold your hand. I want to hold your hand. 2. Oh,
Gtr. 1
Verse
G5 G6 G5 D5 D6 D5 D6 E Open 6 E5 B7 E Open 6
(2.) please say to me and let me be your man. And
(3. 4.) you got that some - thing I think you'll un - der - stand. When
Gtr. 1
(2°)
Gtr. 3 plays Fig. 1
full

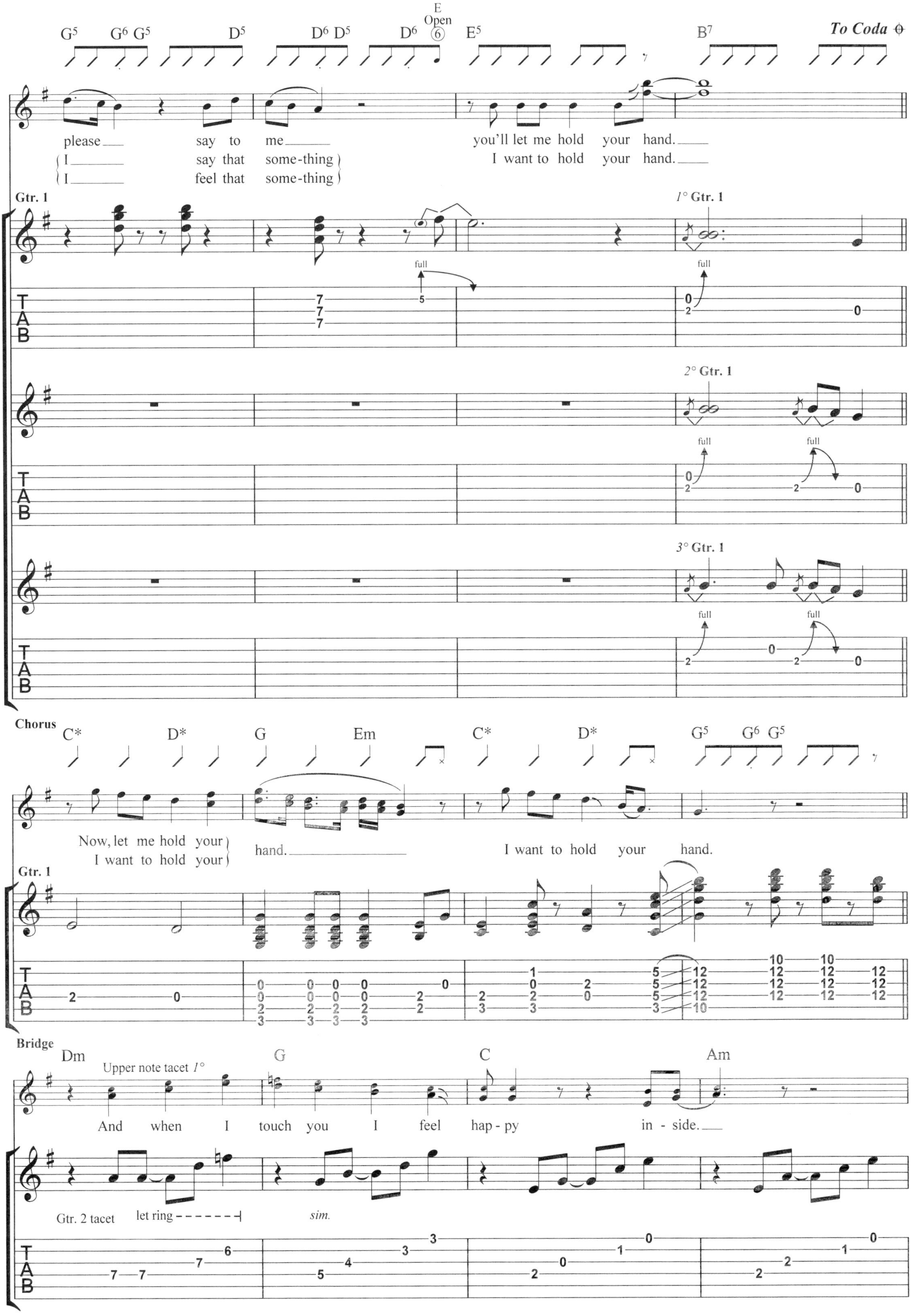

G5 G6 G5 D5 D6 D5 D6 E Open 6 E5 B7
To Coda
please say to me you'll let me hold your hand.
I say that some-thing I want to hold your hand.
I feel that some-thing
Gtr. 1
full
1° Gtr. 1
2° Gtr. 1
3° Gtr. 1
Chorus
C* D* G Em C* D* G5 G6 G5
Now, let me hold your
I want to hold your
hand.
I want to hold your hand.
Gtr. 1
Bridge
Dm G C Am
Upper note tacet 1°
And when I touch you I feel hap-py in-side.
Gtr. 2 tacet
let ring
sim.

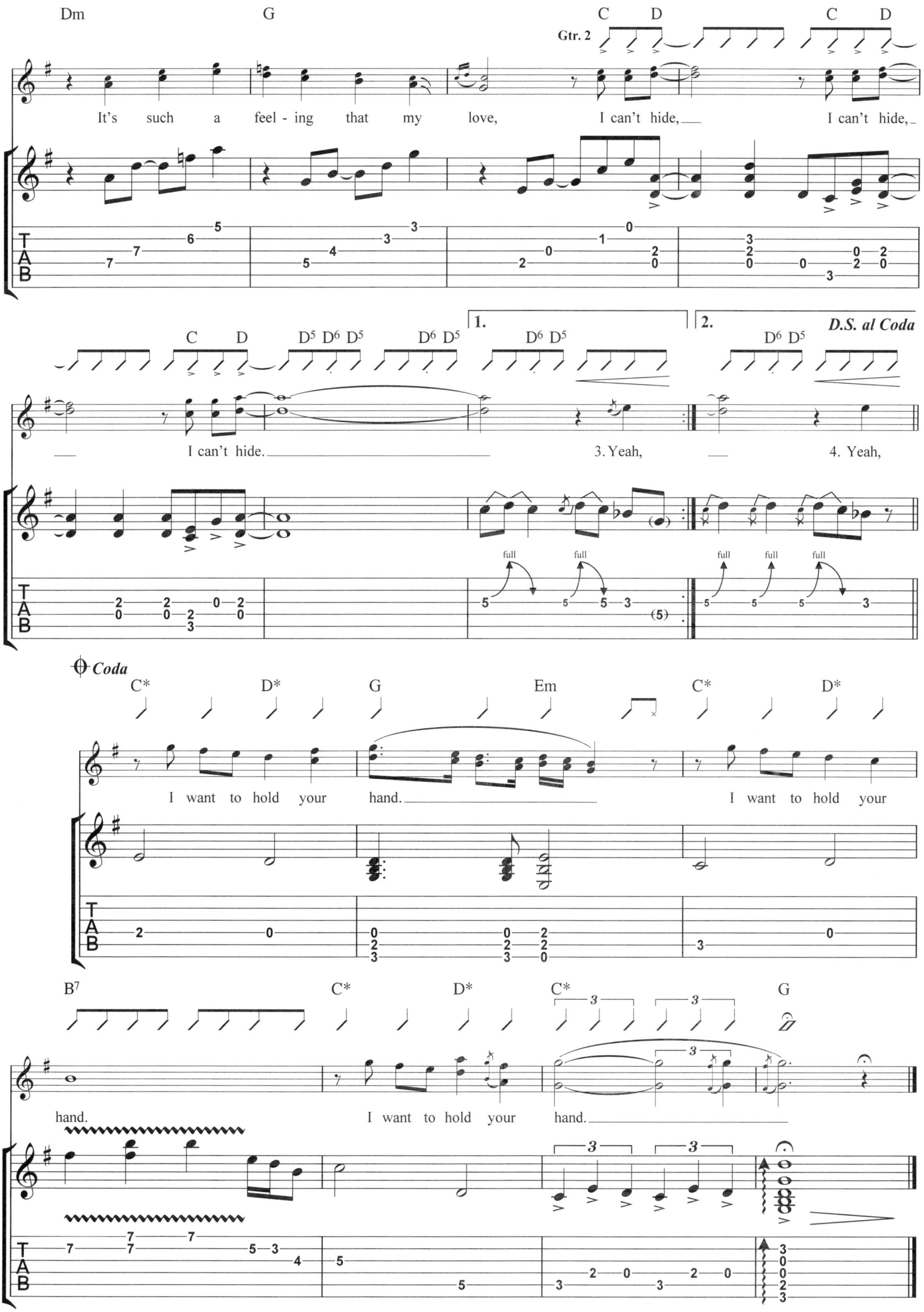
Dm G C D C D
Gtr. 2
It's such a feel - ing that my love, I can't hide, I can't hide,
C D D5 D6 D5 D6 D5 D6 D5 D6 D5
1. 2. D.S. al Coda
I can't hide. 3. Yeah, 4. Yeah,
full full full full full
Coda
C* D* G Em C* D*
I want to hold your hand. I want to hold your
B7 C* D* C* G
hand. I want to hold your hand.

CAN'T BUY ME LOVE

Words & Music by John Lennon & Paul McCartney

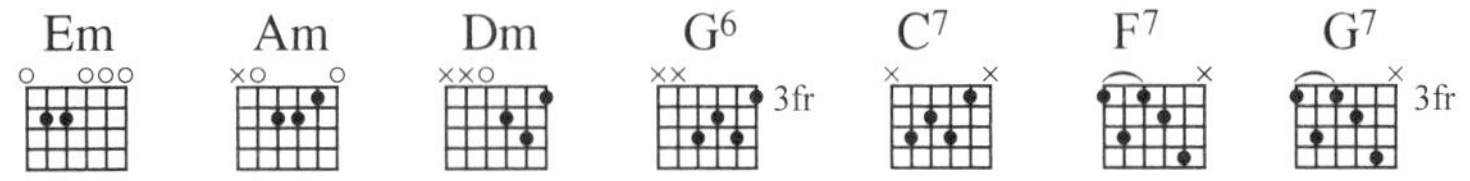

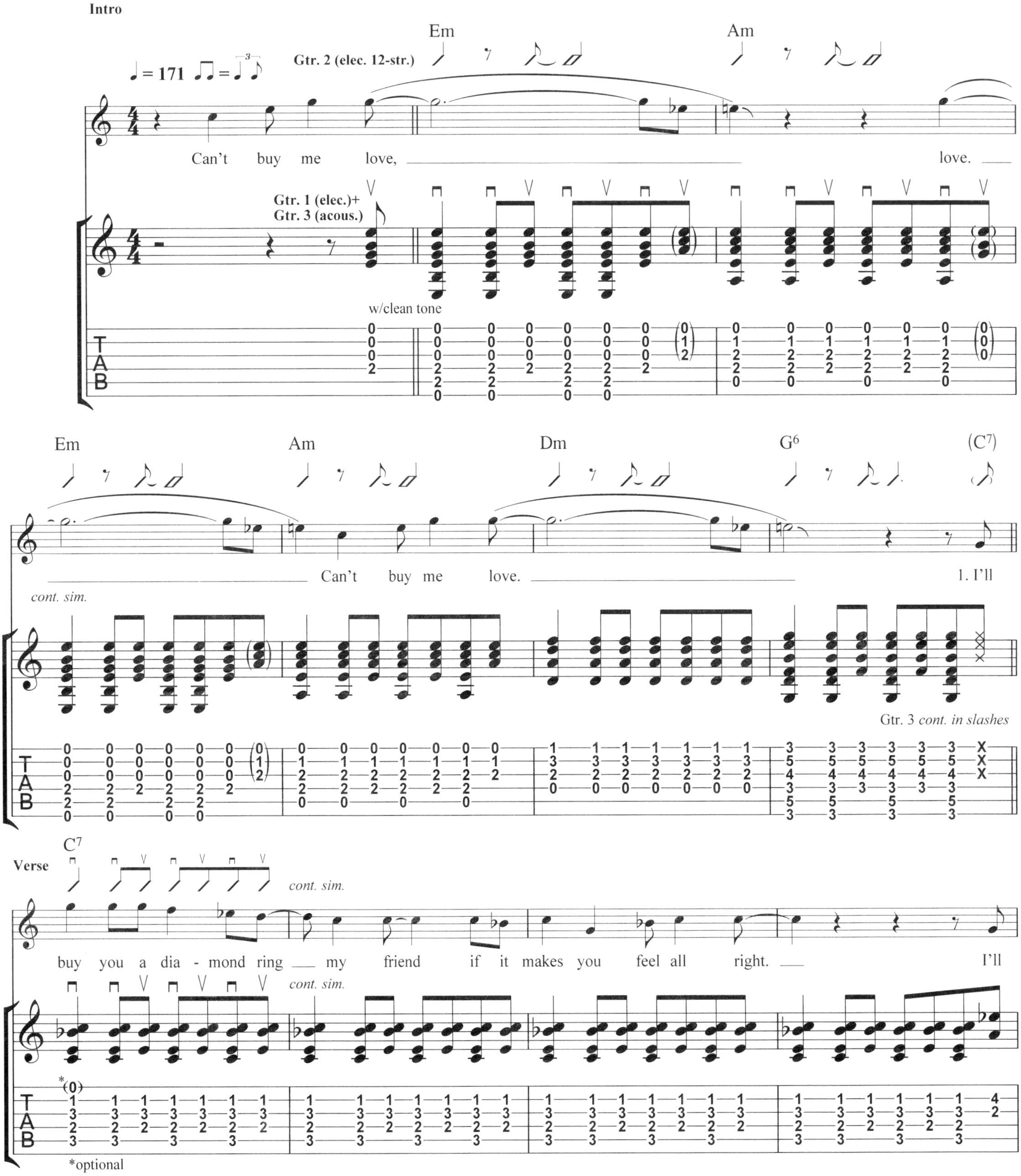

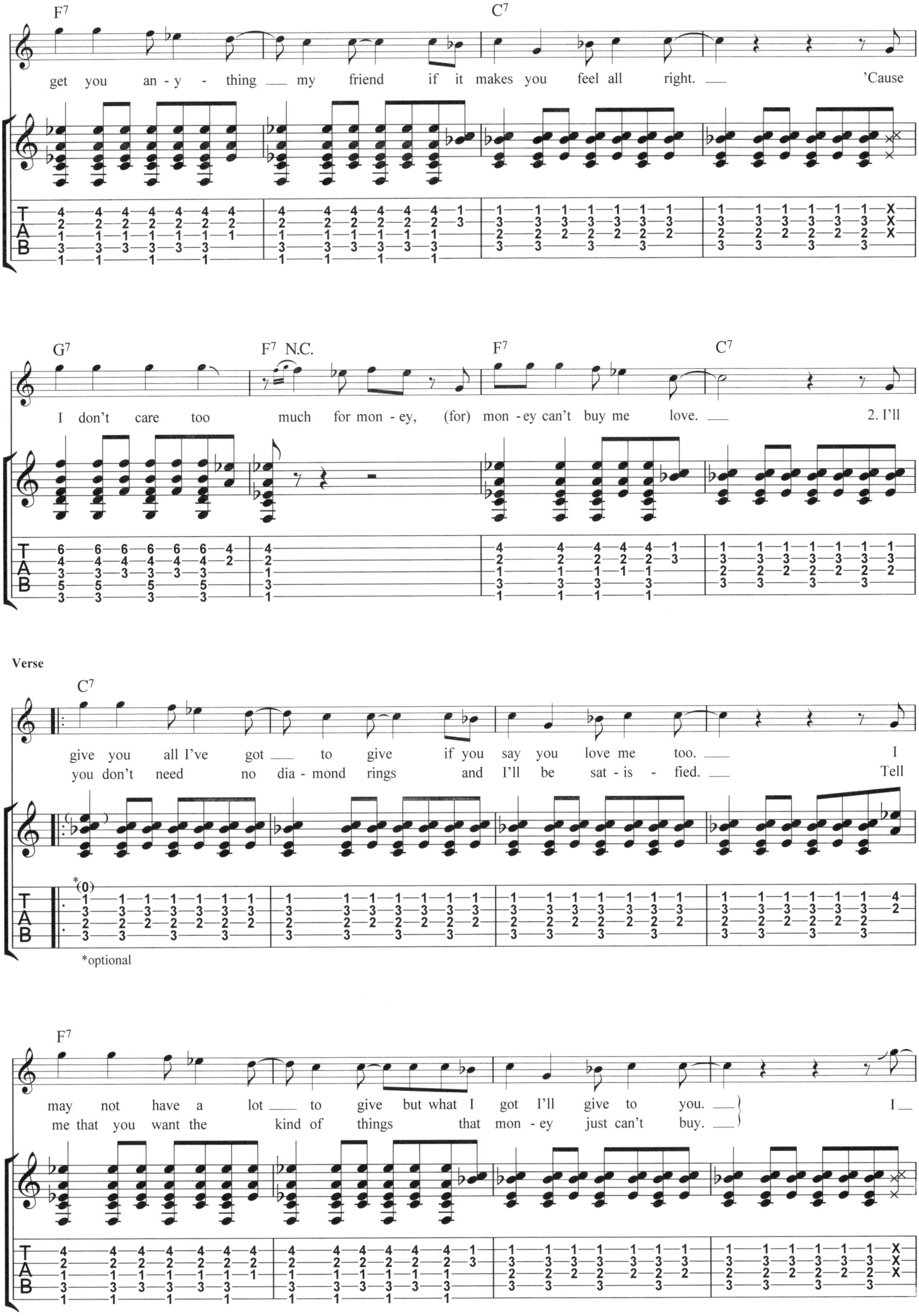
F7 C7
get you an - y - thing my friend if it makes you feel all right. 'Cause
G7 F7 N.C. F7 C7
I don't care too much for mon - ey, (for) mon - ey can't buy me love. 2. I'll
Verse
C7
give you all I've got to give if you say you love me too. I
you don't need no dia - mond rings and I'll be sat - is - fied. Tell
*optional
F7
may not have a lot to give but what I got I'll give to you. I
me that you want the kind of things that mon - ey just can't buy.

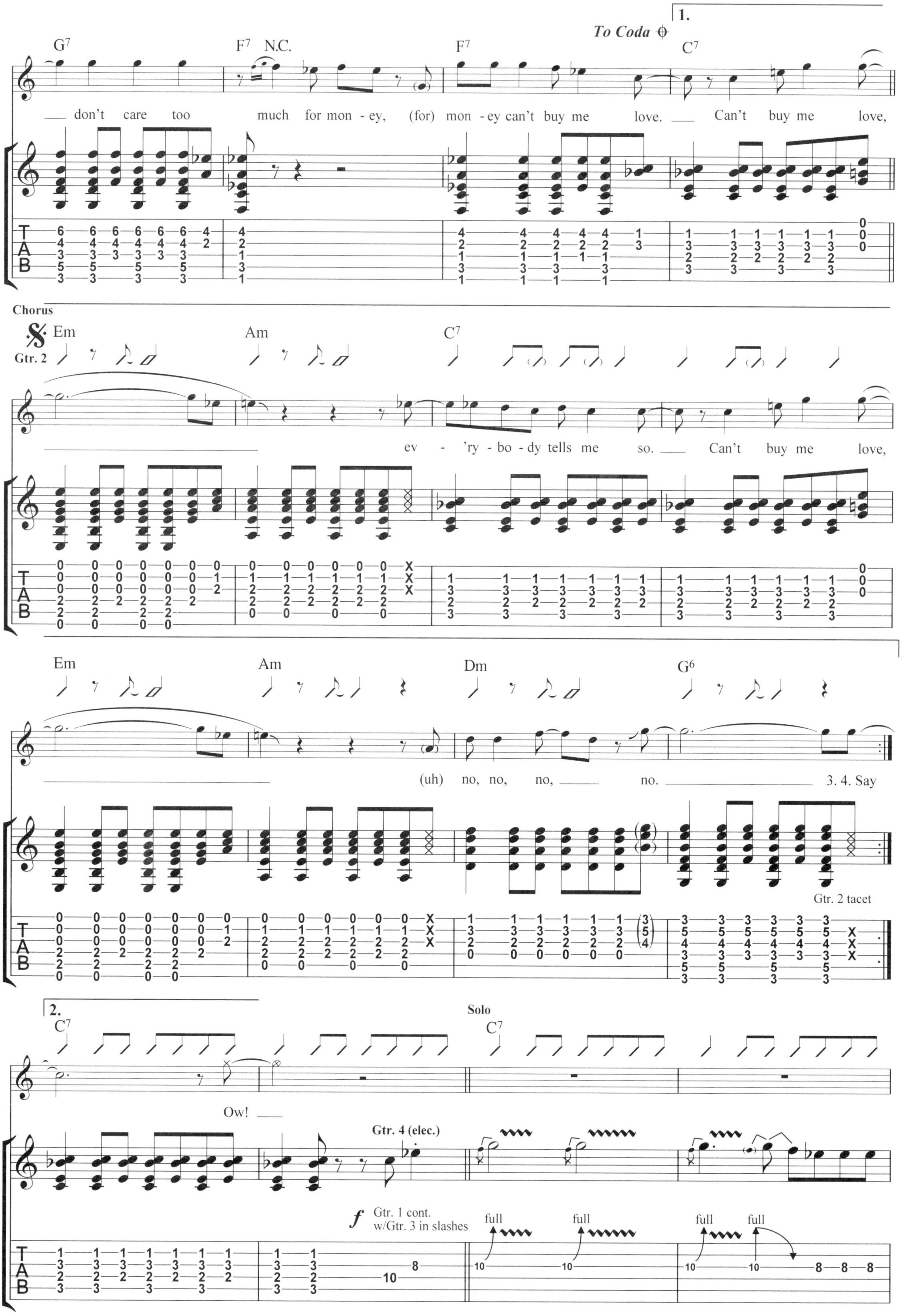
To Coda
1.
G7 F7 N.C. F7 C7
don't care too much for mon - ey, (for) mon - ey can't buy me love. Can't buy me love,
Chorus
Em Am C7
Gtr. 2
ev - 'ry - bo - dy tells me so. Can't buy me love,
Em Am Dm G6
(uh) no, no, no, no. 3. 4. Say
Gtr. 2 tacet
2.
C7
Solo
C7
Ow!
Gtr. 4 (elec.)
f
Gtr. 1 cont. w/Gtr. 3 in slashes
full full full full

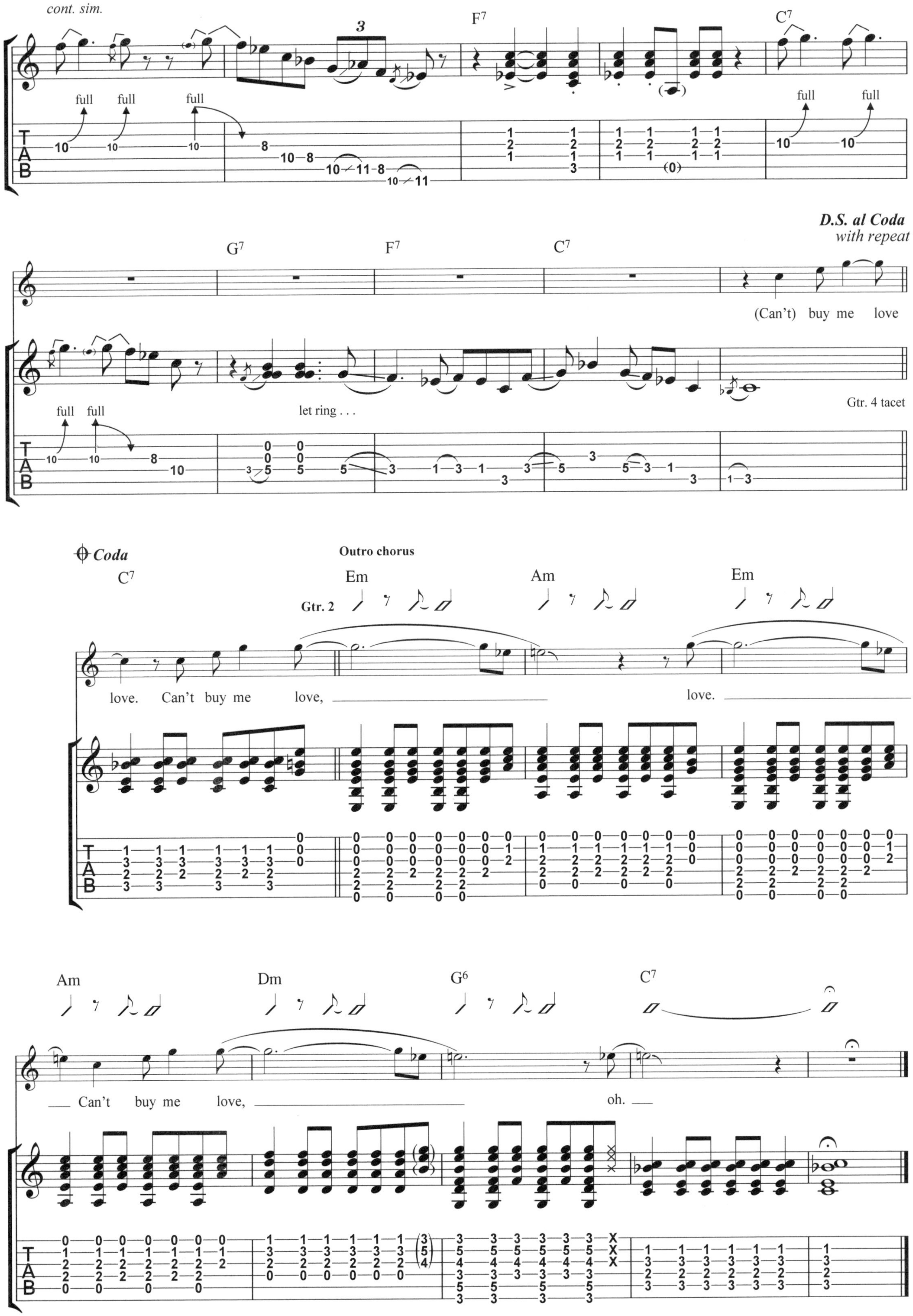
cont. sim.
F7
C7
full full full
full full
G7
F7
C7
D.S. al Coda
with repeat
(Can't) buy me love
full full
let ring . . .
Gtr. 4 tacet
Coda
Outro chorus
C7
Em
Am
Em
Gtr. 2
love. Can't buy me love, love.
Am
Dm
G6
C7
Can't buy me love, oh.

A HARD DAY'S NIGHT

Words & Music by John Lennon & Paul McCartney

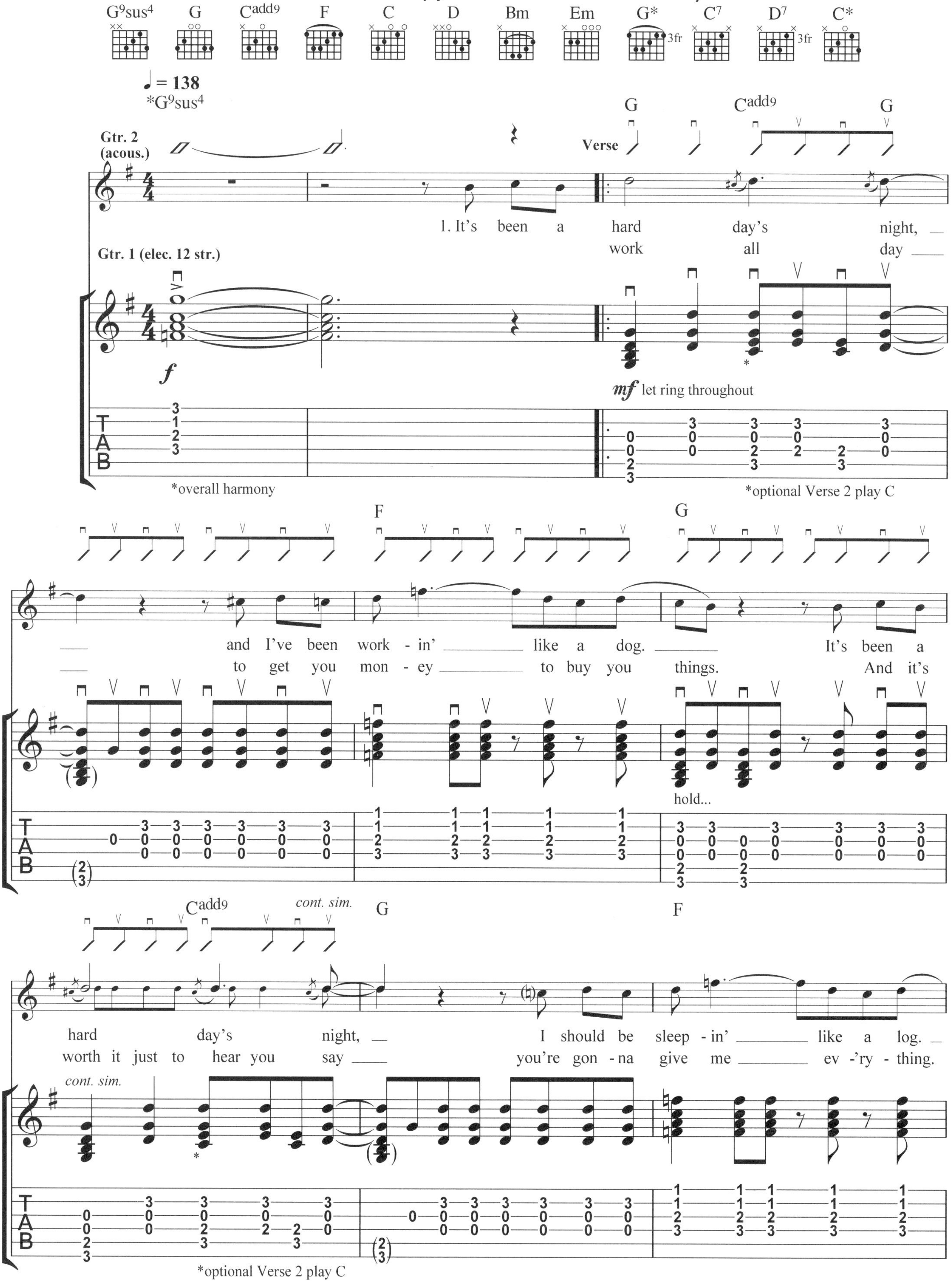

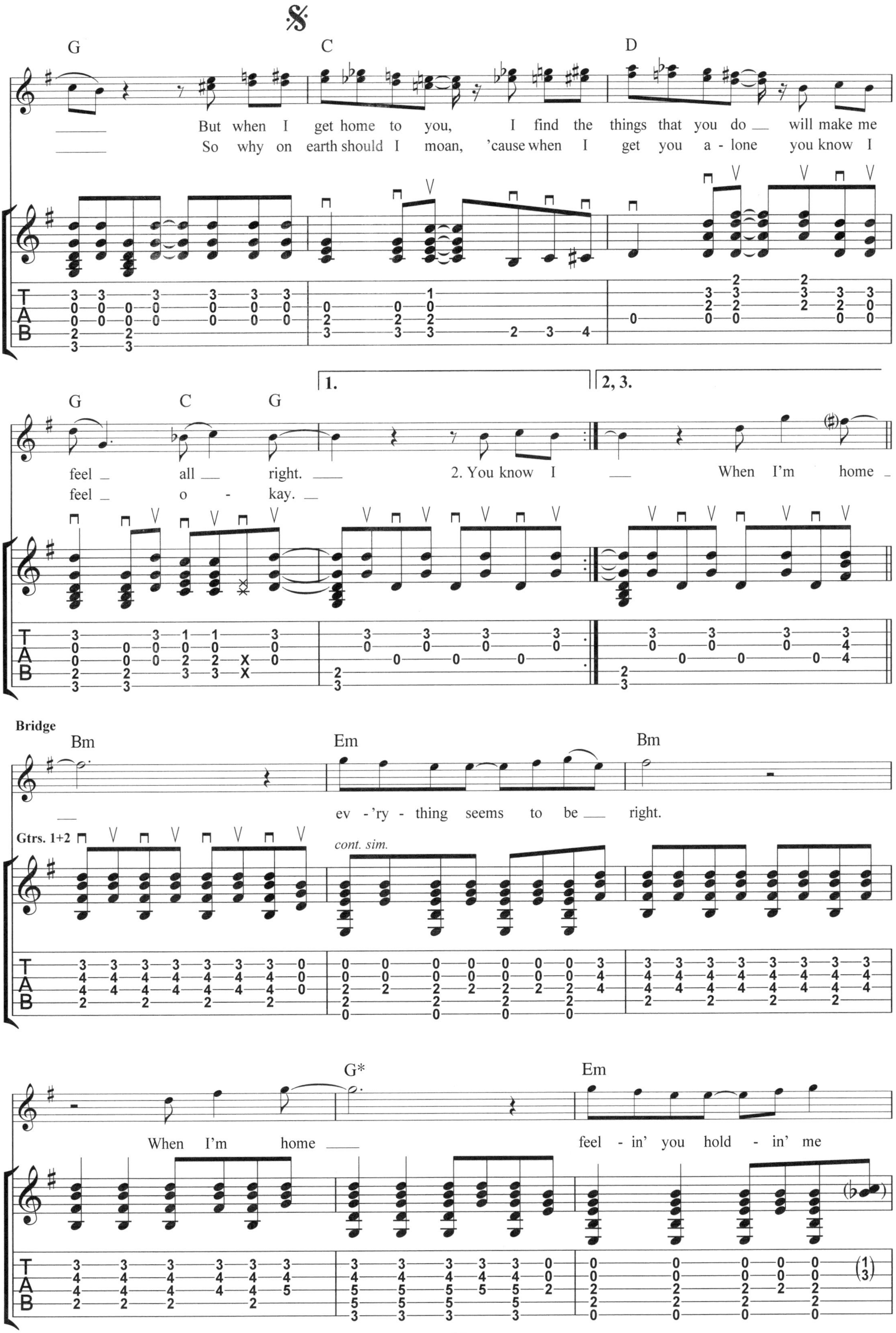
G C D
But when I get home to you, I find the things that you do will make me
So why on earth should I moan, 'cause when I get you a - lone you know I
1.
2, 3.
G C G
feel all right. 2. You know I When I'm home
feel o - kay.
Bridge
Bm Em Bm
ev - 'ry - thing seems to be right.
Gtrs. 1+2
cont. sim.
G* Em
When I'm home feel - in' you hold - in' me

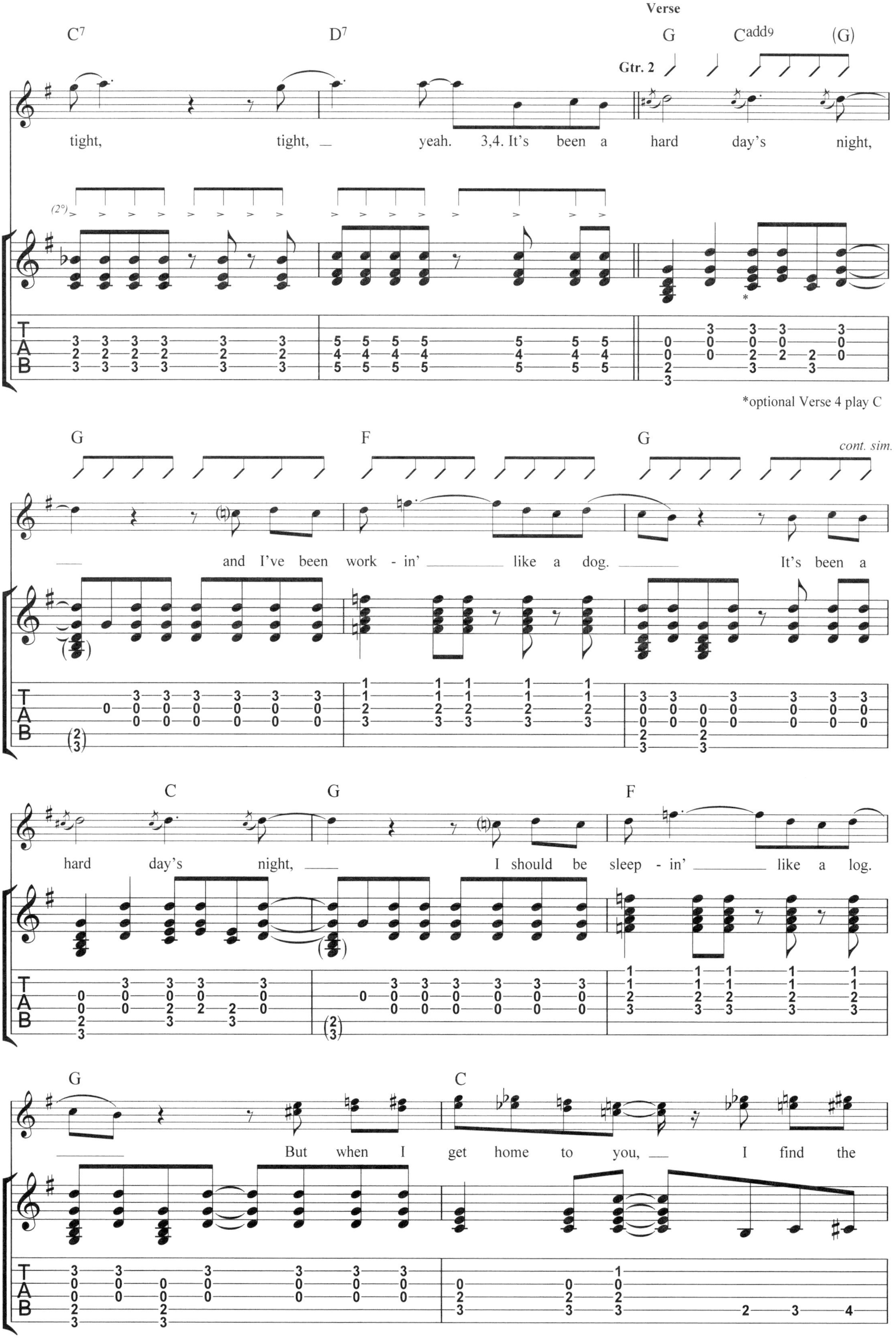
Verse
C7 D7 G Cadd9 (G)
Gtr. 2
tight, tight, yeah. 3,4. It's been a hard day's night,
(2°)
T A B
*optional Verse 4 play C
G F G
cont. sim.
and I've been work - in' like a dog. It's been a
C G F
hard day's night, I should be sleep - in' like a log.
G C
But when I get home to you, I find the

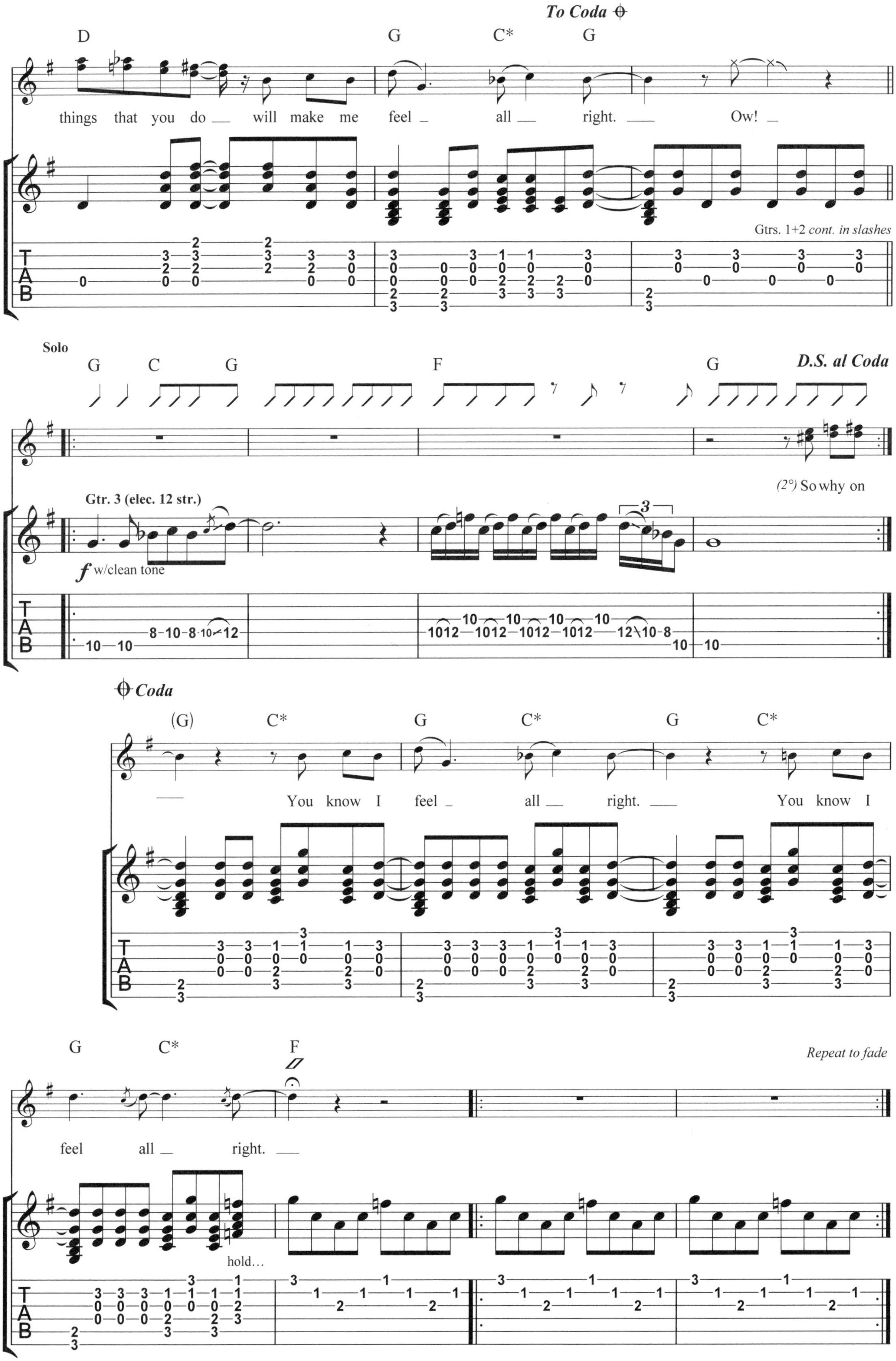
To Coda
D G C* G
things that you do will make me feel all right. Ow!
Gtrs. 1+2 cont. in slashes
Solo
G C G F G
D.S. al Coda
(2°) So why on
Gtr. 3 (elec. 12 str.)
f w/clean tone
Coda
(G) C* G C* G C*
You know I feel all right. You know I
G C* F
Repeat to fade
feel all right.
hold…

I FEEL FINE

Words & Music by John Lennon & Paul McCartney

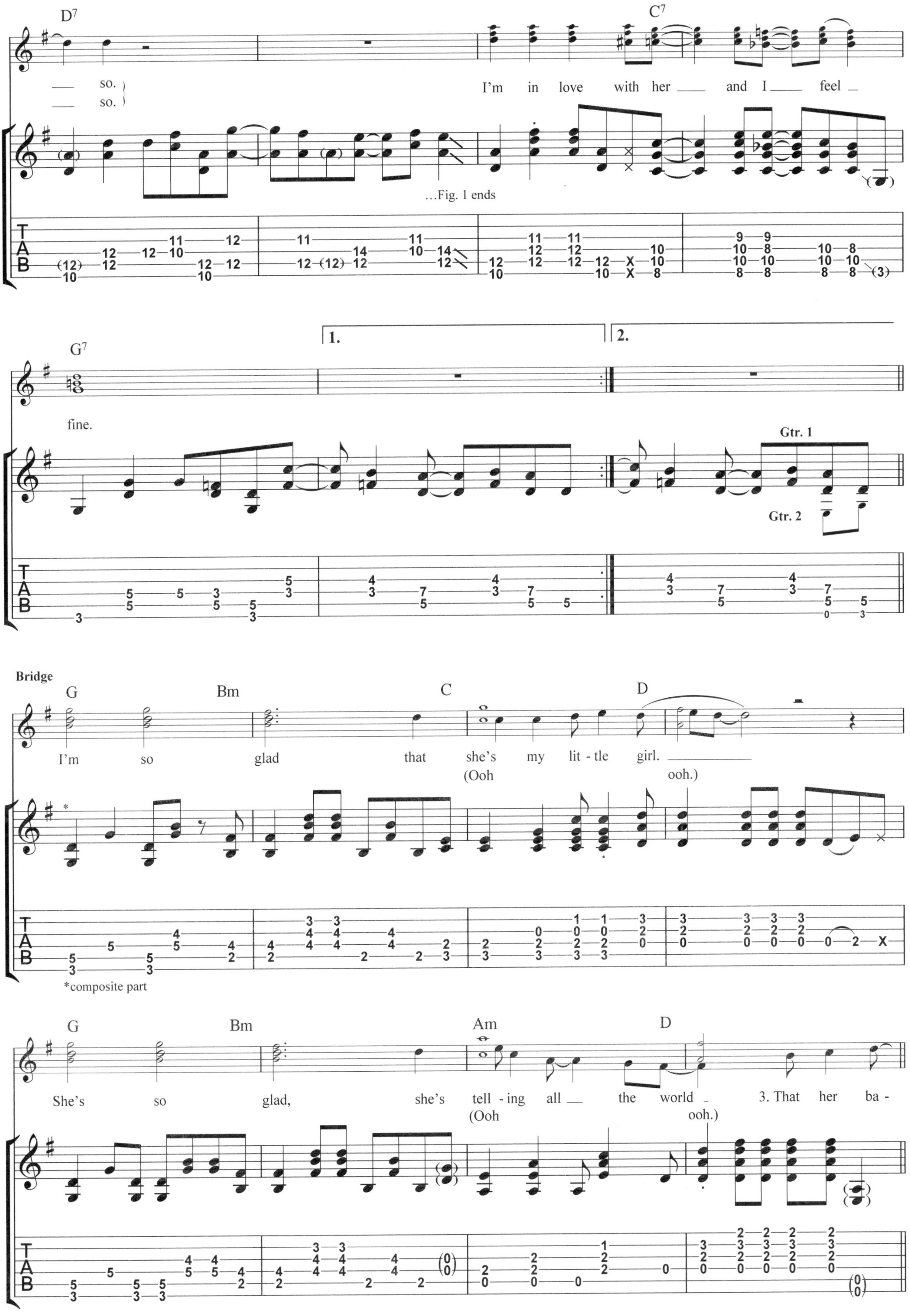
D7
C7
so.
so.
I'm in love with her and I feel
…Fig. 1 ends
T
A
B
G7
1.
2.
fine.
Gtr. 1
Gtr. 2
Bridge
G
Bm
C
D
I'm so glad that she's my lit - tle girl.
(Ooh ooh.)
*composite part
G
Bm
Am
D
She's so glad, she's tell - ing all the world
3. That her ba -
(Ooh ooh.)

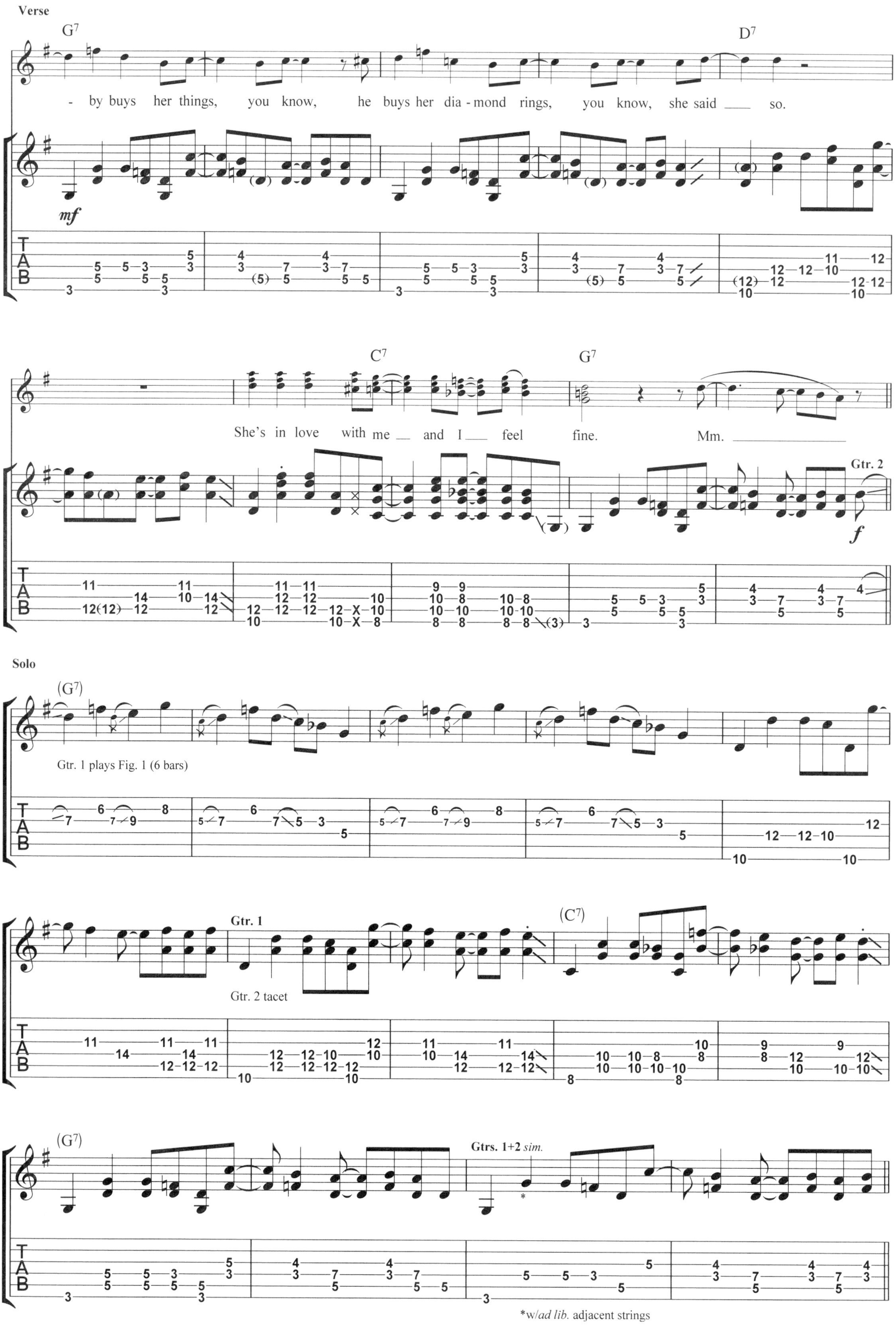
Verse
G7
D7
- by buys her things, you know, he buys her dia - mond rings, you know, she said ___ so.
mf
C7
G7
She's in love with me __ and I ___ feel fine. Mm. ___
Gtr. 2
f
Solo
(G7)
Gtr. 1 plays Fig. 1 (6 bars)
Gtr. 1
Gtr. 2 tacet
(C7)
(G7)
Gtrs. 1+2 sim.
*w/ad lib. adjacent strings

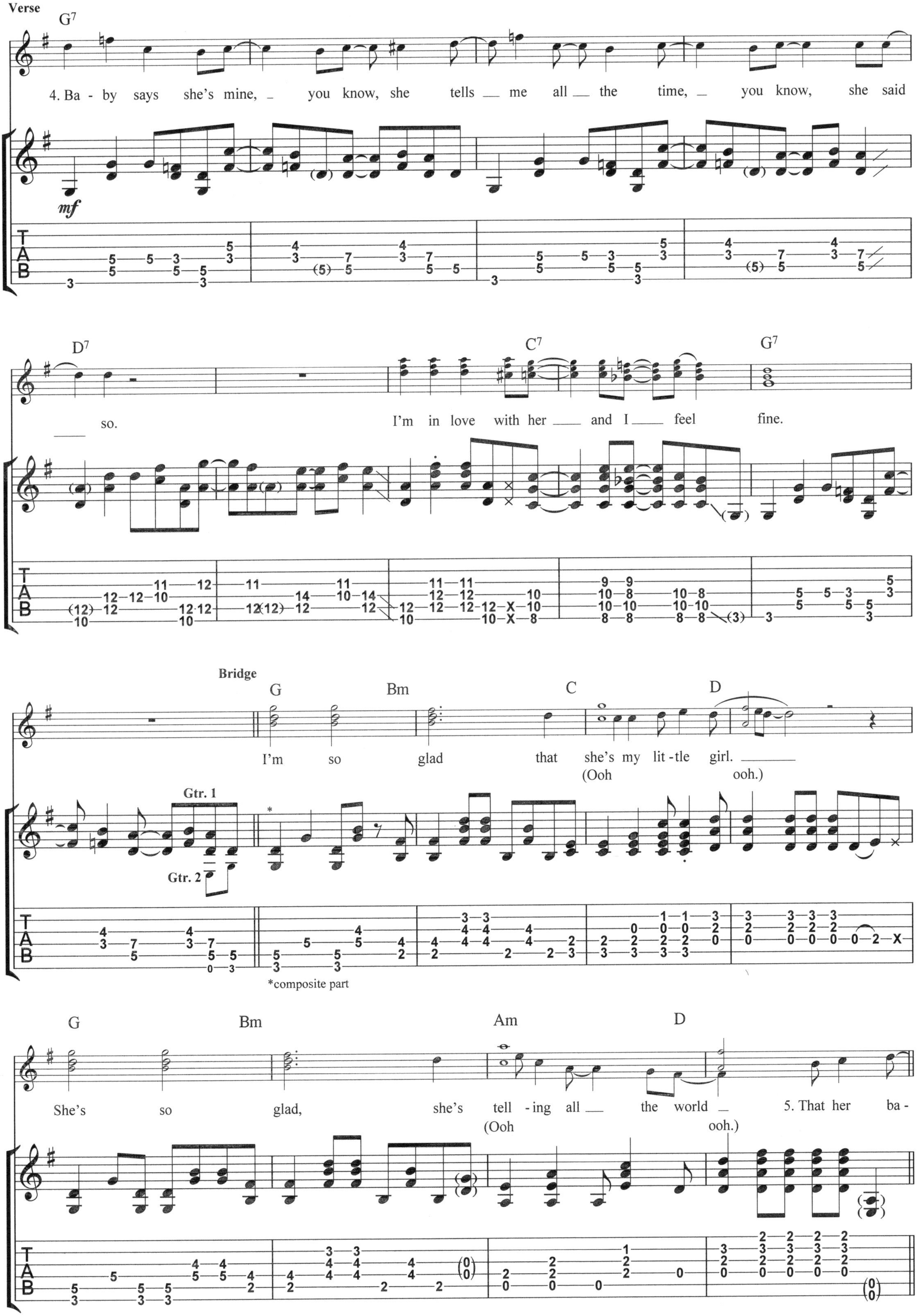
Verse
G7
4. Ba - by says she's mine, you know, she tells me all the time, you know, she said
mf
D7
so.
C7
G7
I'm in love with her and I feel fine.
Bridge
G
Bm
C
D
I'm so glad that she's my lit - tle girl.
(Ooh ooh.)
Gtr. 1
Gtr. 2
*composite part
G
Bm
Am
D
She's so glad, she's tell - ing all the world
(Ooh ooh.)
5. That her ba -

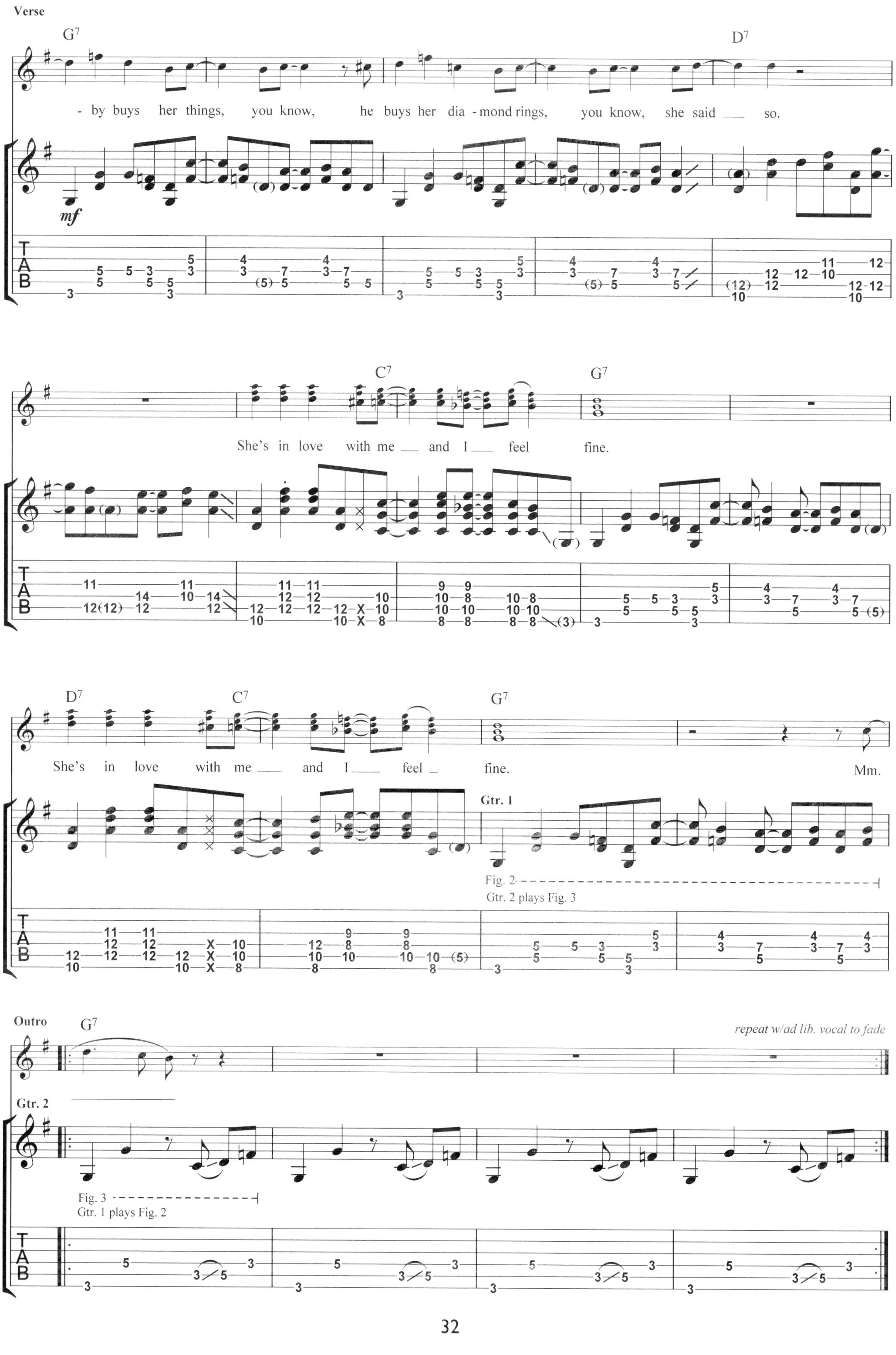
Verse
G7
D7
- by buys her things, you know, he buys her dia - mond rings, you know, she said __ so.
mf
C7
G7
She's in love with me __ and I __ feel fine.
D7
C7
G7
She's in love with me __ and I __ feel _ fine.
Mm.
Gtr. 1
Fig. 2
Gtr. 2 plays Fig. 3
Outro
G7
repeat w/ad lib. vocal to fade
Gtr. 2
Fig. 3
Gtr. 1 plays Fig. 2

TICKET TO RIDE

Words & Music by John Lennon & Paul McCartney

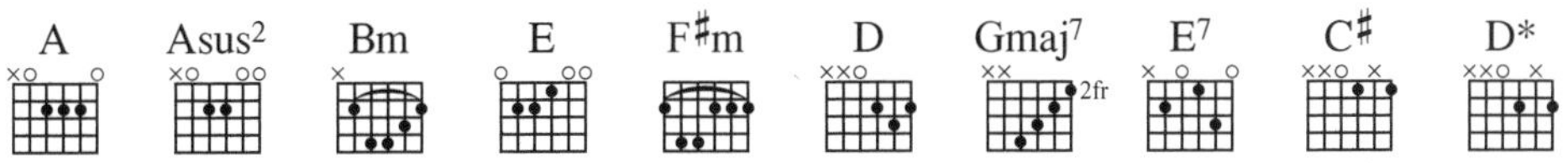

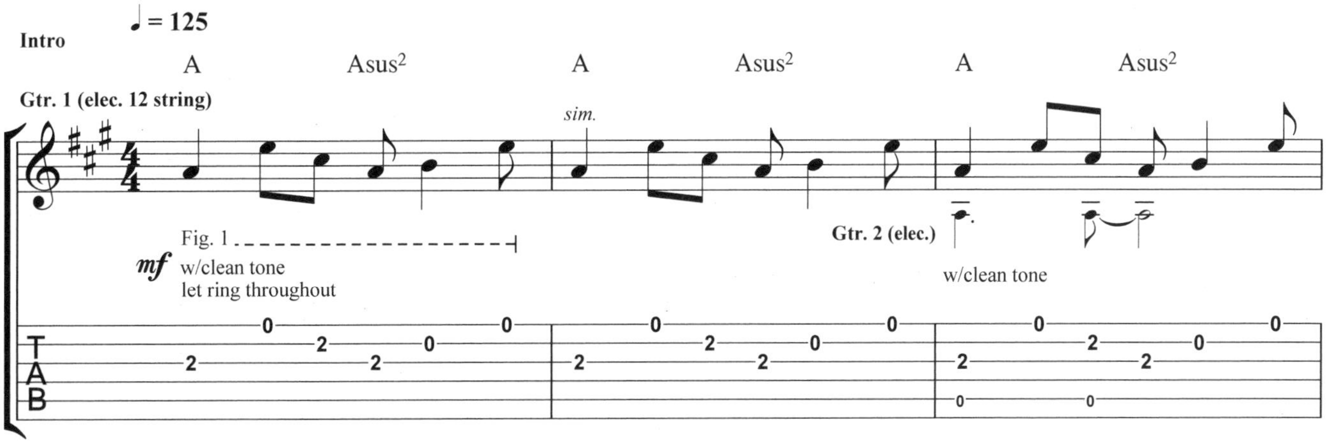

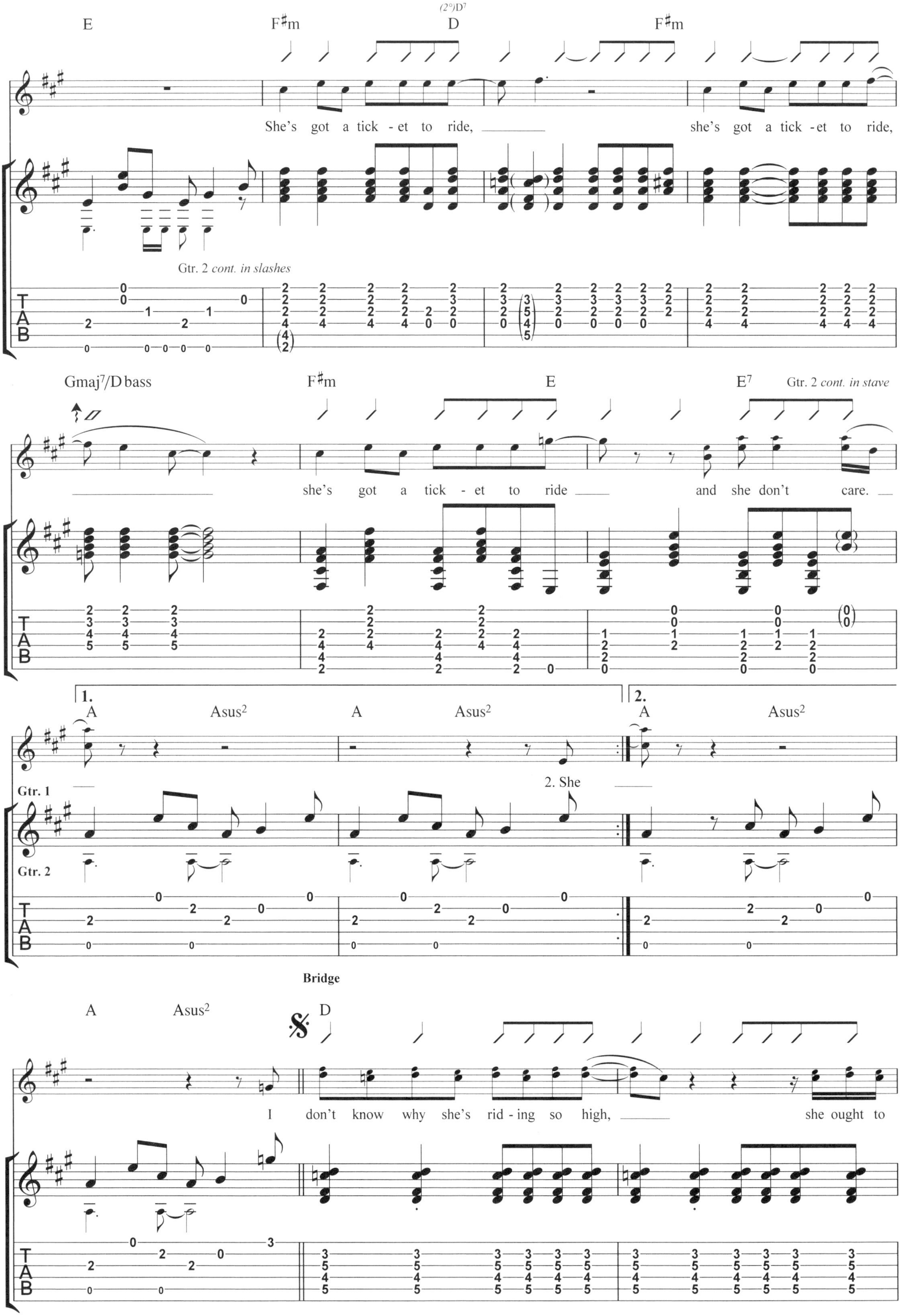
E F♯m (2°)D7 D F♯m
She's got a tick - et to ride, she's got a tick - et to ride,
Gtr. 2 cont. in slashes
Gmaj7/D bass F♯m E E7 Gtr. 2 cont. in stave
she's got a tick - et to ride and she don't care.
1. A Asus2 A Asus2 2. A Asus2
2. She
Gtr. 1
Gtr. 2
Bridge
A Asus2 D
I don't know why she's rid - ing so high, she ought to

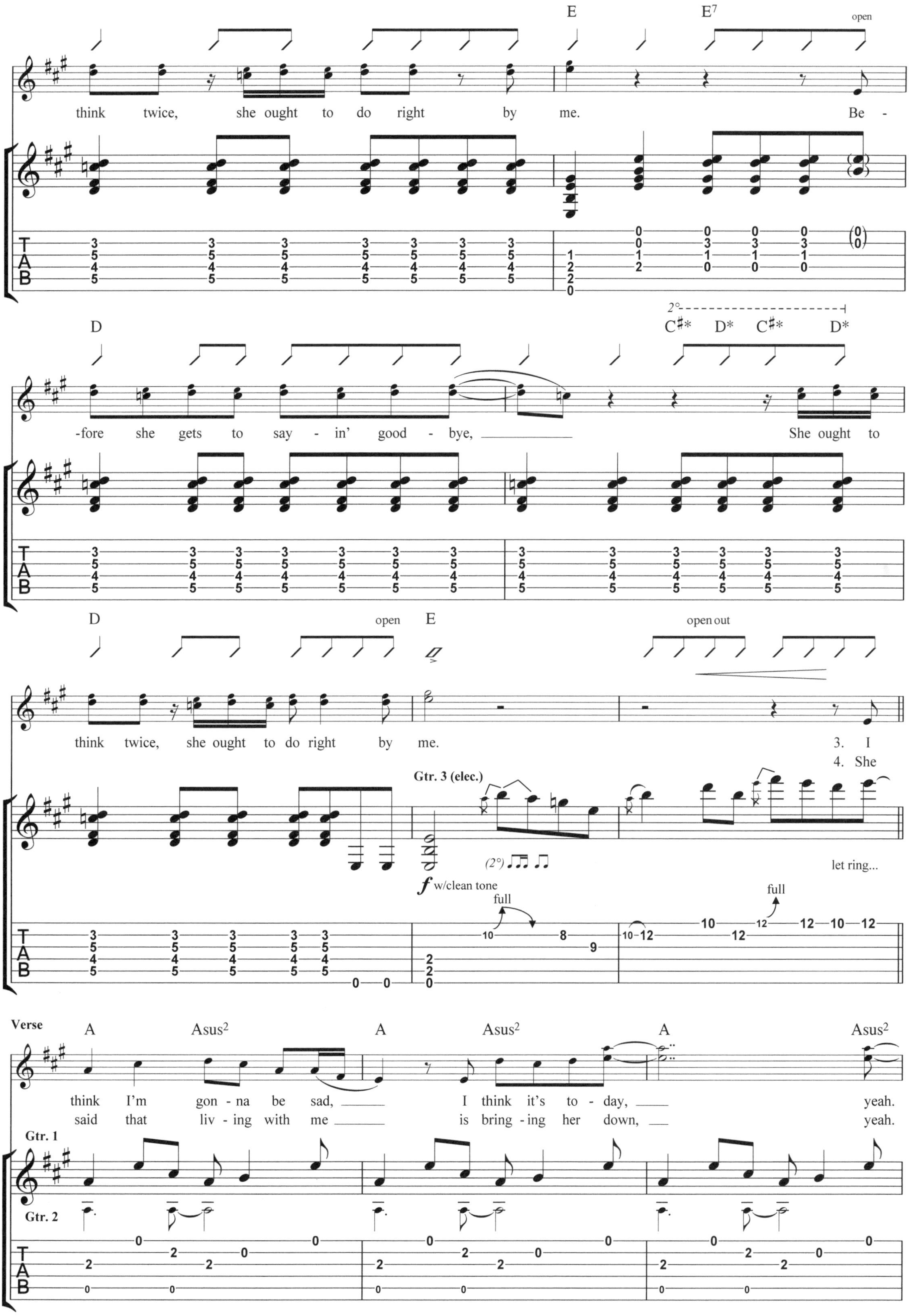
E E7 open
think twice, she ought to do right by me. Be -
D 2°. C♯* D* C♯* D*
-fore she gets to say - in' good - bye, She ought to
D open E open out
think twice, she ought to do right by me.
3. I
4. She
Gtr. 3 (elec.)
(2°)
f w/clean tone
let ring...
full
full
Verse
A Asus2 A Asus2 A Asus2
think I'm gon - na be sad, I think it's to - day, yeah.
said that liv - ing with me is bring - ing her down, yeah.
Gtr. 1
Gtr. 2
TAB

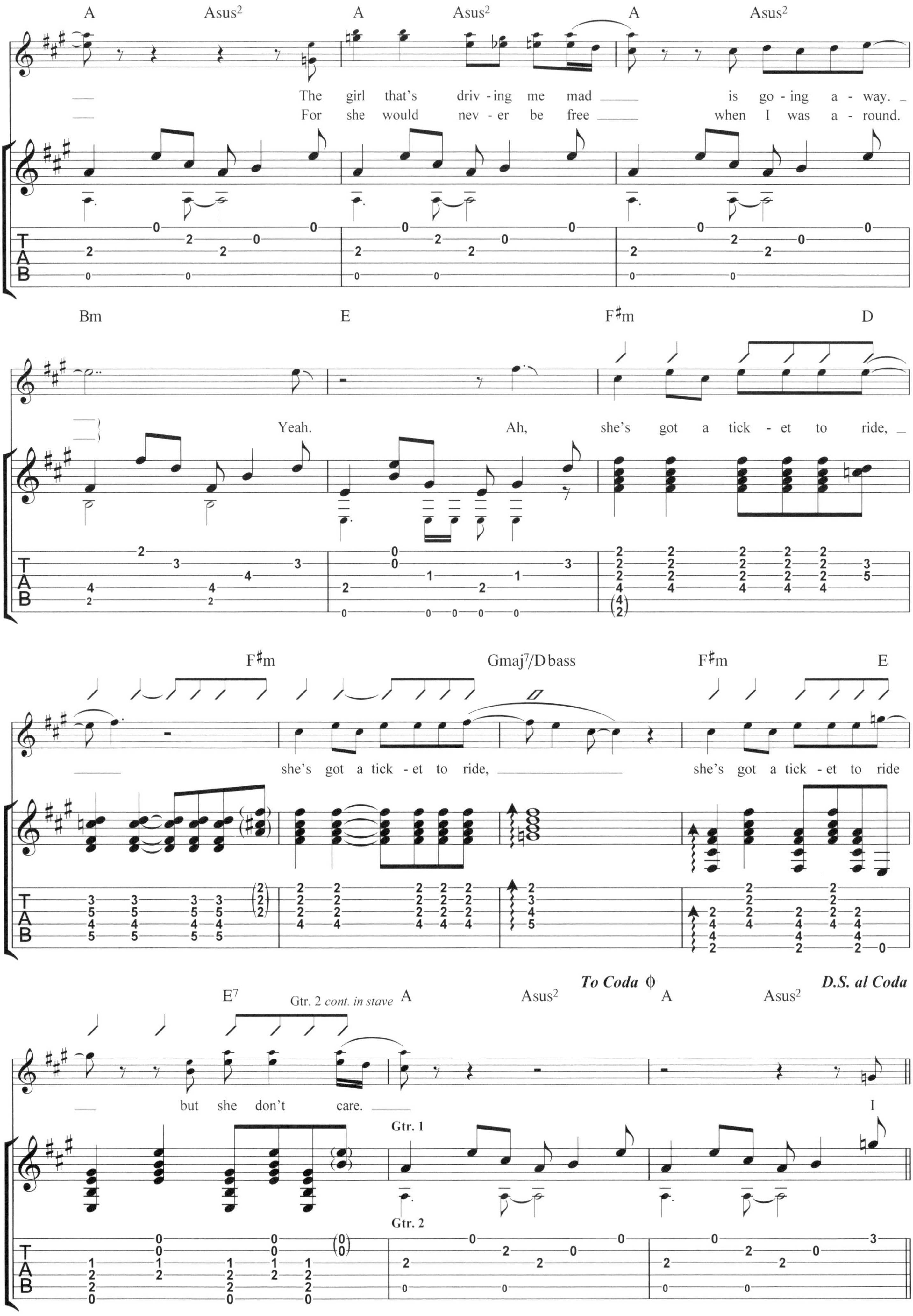
A Asus2 A Asus2 A Asus2
The girl that's driv - ing me mad is go - ing a - way.
For she would nev - er be free when I was a - round.
Bm E F♯m D
Yeah. Ah, she's got a tick - et to ride,
F♯m Gmaj7/D bass F♯m E
she's got a tick - et to ride, she's got a tick - et to ride
E7 Gtr. 2 cont. in stave A Asus2 To Coda A Asus2 D.S. al Coda
but she don't care. I
Gtr. 1
Gtr. 2

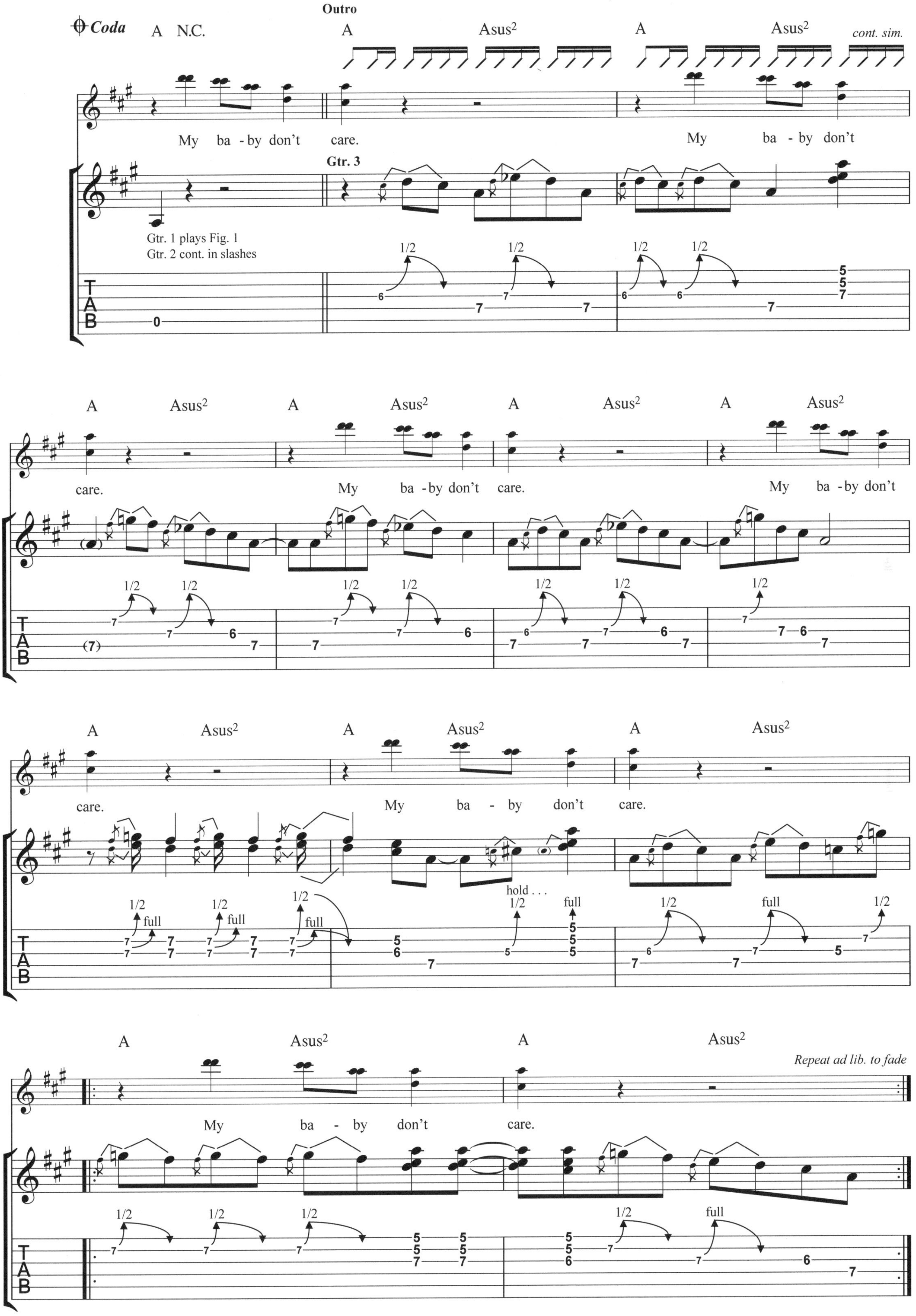
Coda
Outro
A N.C.
A Asus2 A Asus2
cont. sim.
My baby don't care.
My baby don't care.
Gtr. 3
Gtr. 1 plays Fig. 1
Gtr. 2 cont. in slashes
1/2
full
hold...
Repeat ad lib. to fade
T
A
B

EIGHT DAYS A WEEK

Words & Music by John Lennon & Paul McCartney

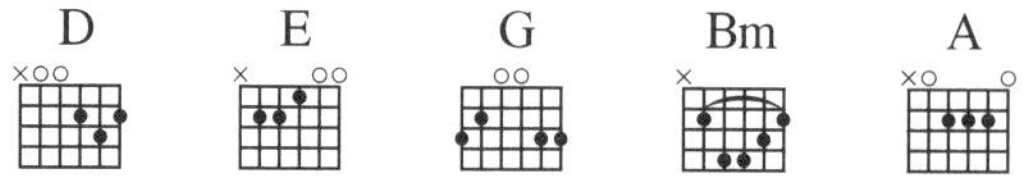

Intro

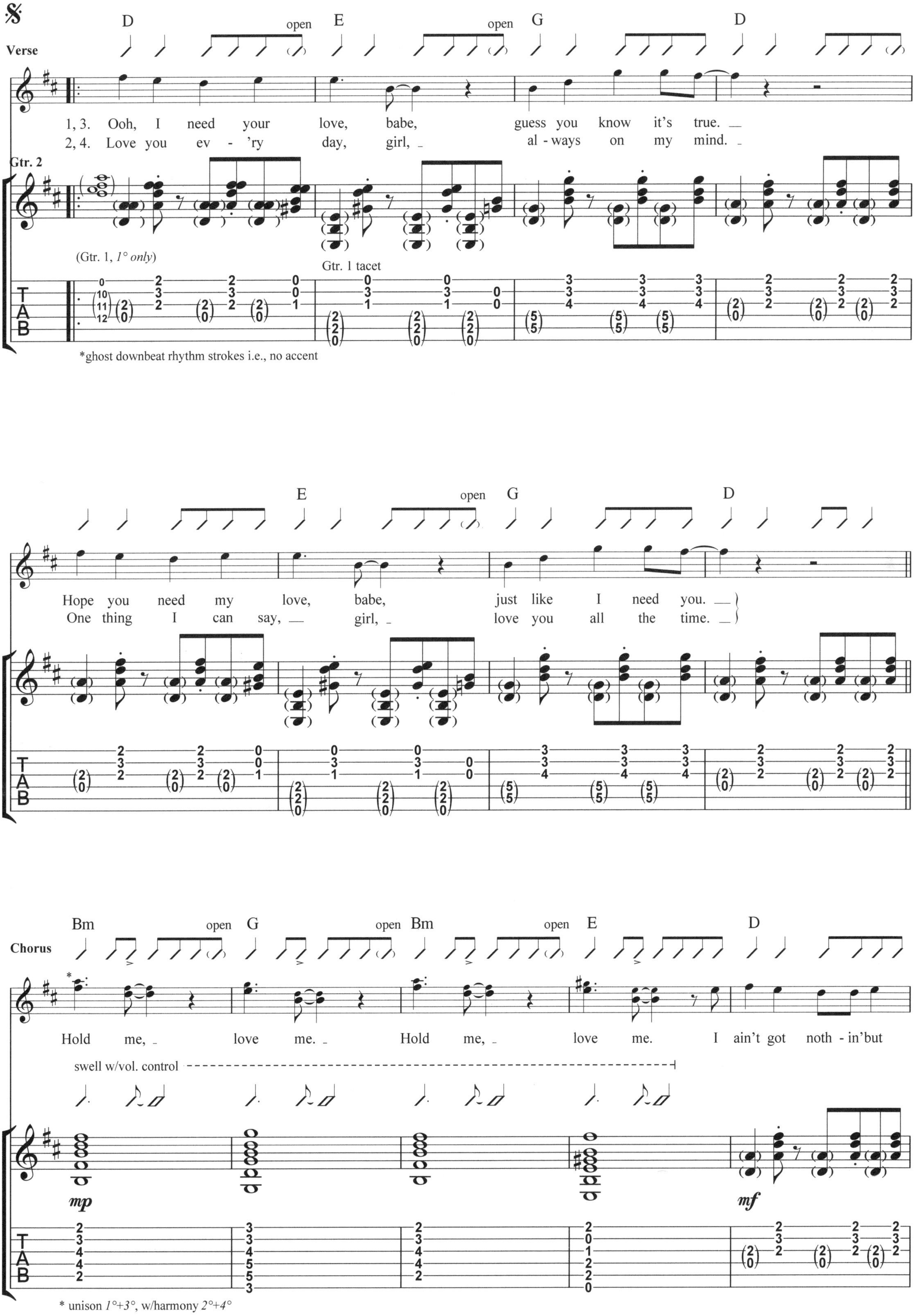
Verse
D
open
E
open
G
D
1, 3. Ooh, I need your love, babe, guess you know it's true.
2, 4. Love you ev - 'ry day, girl, al - ways on my mind.
Gtr. 2
(Gtr. 1, 1° only)
Gtr. 1 tacet
*ghost downbeat rhythm strokes i.e., no accent
E
open
G
D
Hope you need my love, babe, just like I need you.
One thing I can say, girl, love you all the time.
Chorus
Bm
open
G
open
Bm
open
E
D
Hold me, love me. Hold me, love me. I ain't got noth - in'but
swell w/vol. control
mp
mf
* unison 1°+3°, w/harmony 2°+4°

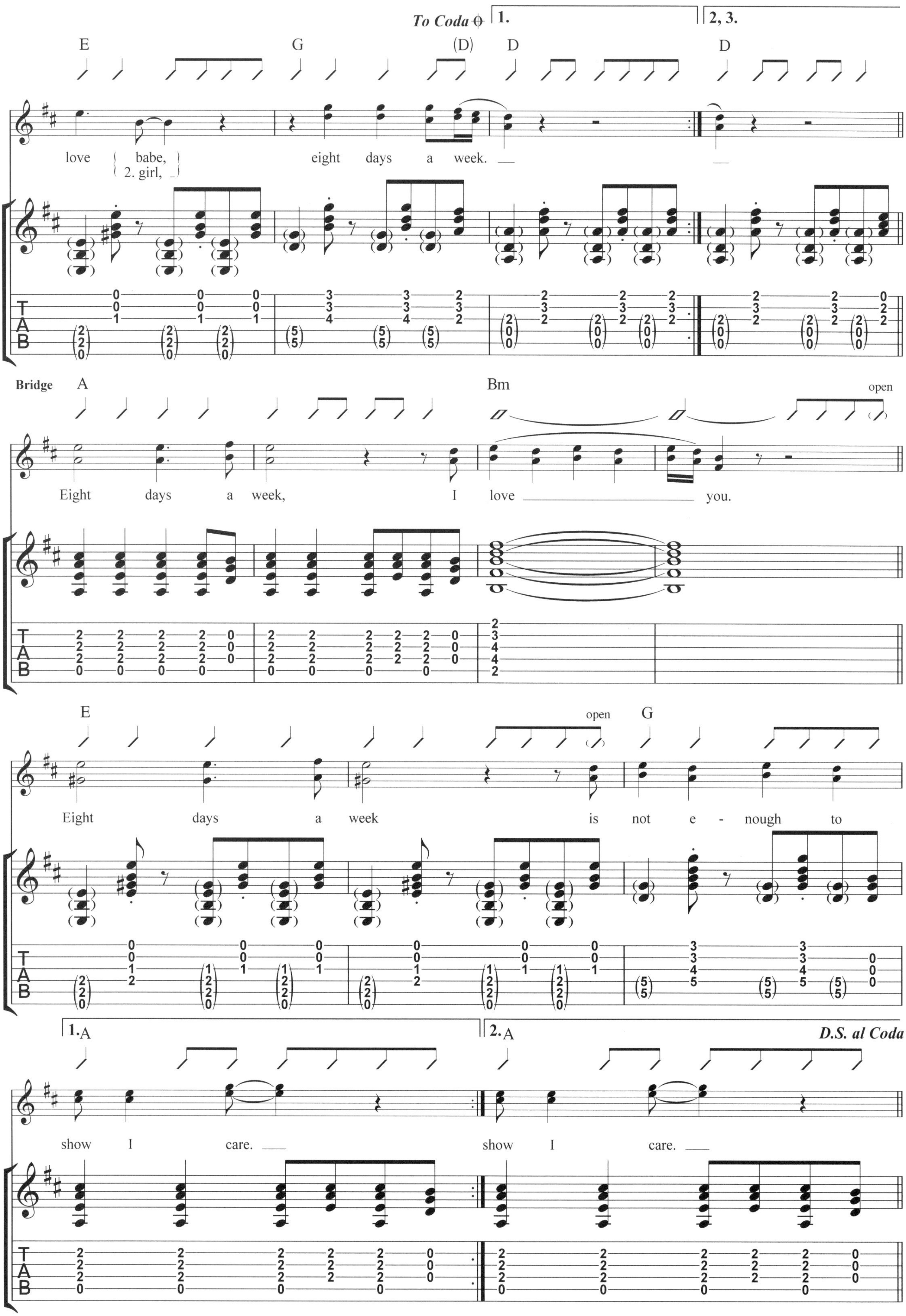
To Coda
1.
2, 3.
E
G
(D)
D
D
love
babe,
2. girl,
eight
days
a
week.
Bridge
A
Bm
open
Eight
days
a
week,
I
love
you.
E
open
G
Eight
days
a
week
is
not
e
-
nough
to
1.A
2.A
D.S. al Coda
show
I
care.
show
I
care.

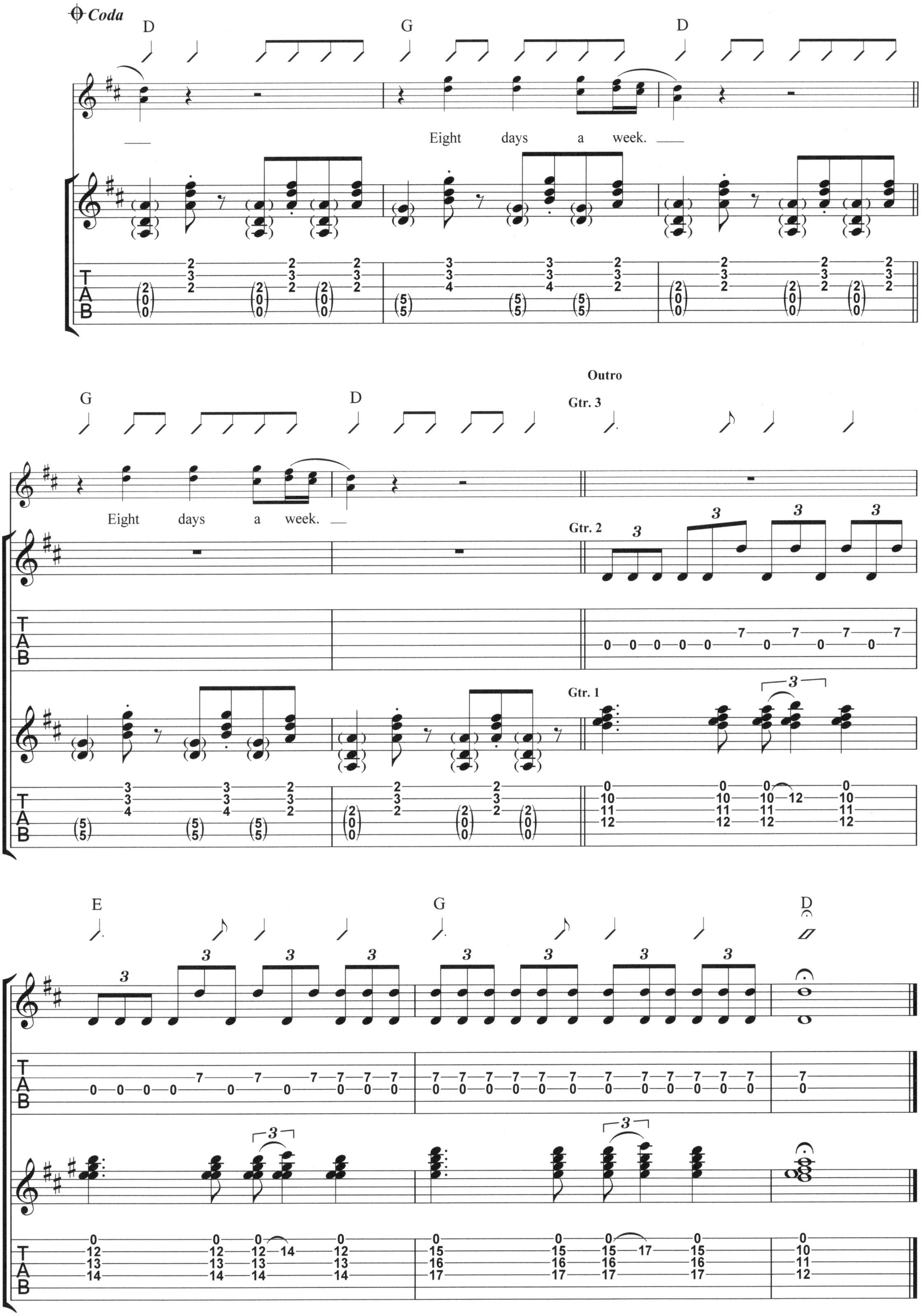
Coda
D
G
D
Eight days a week.
G
D
Eight days a week.
Outro
Gtr. 3
Gtr. 2
Gtr. 1
E
G
D

HELP!

Words & Music by John Lennon & Paul McCartney

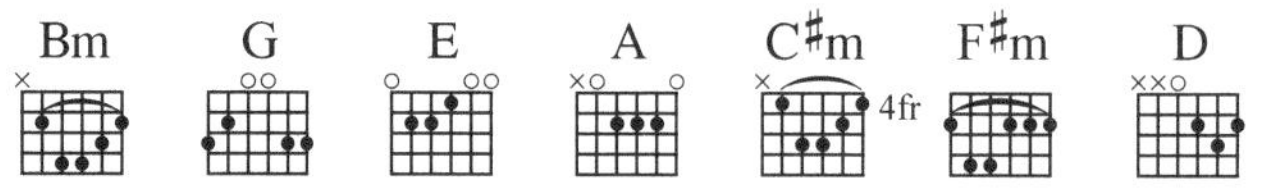

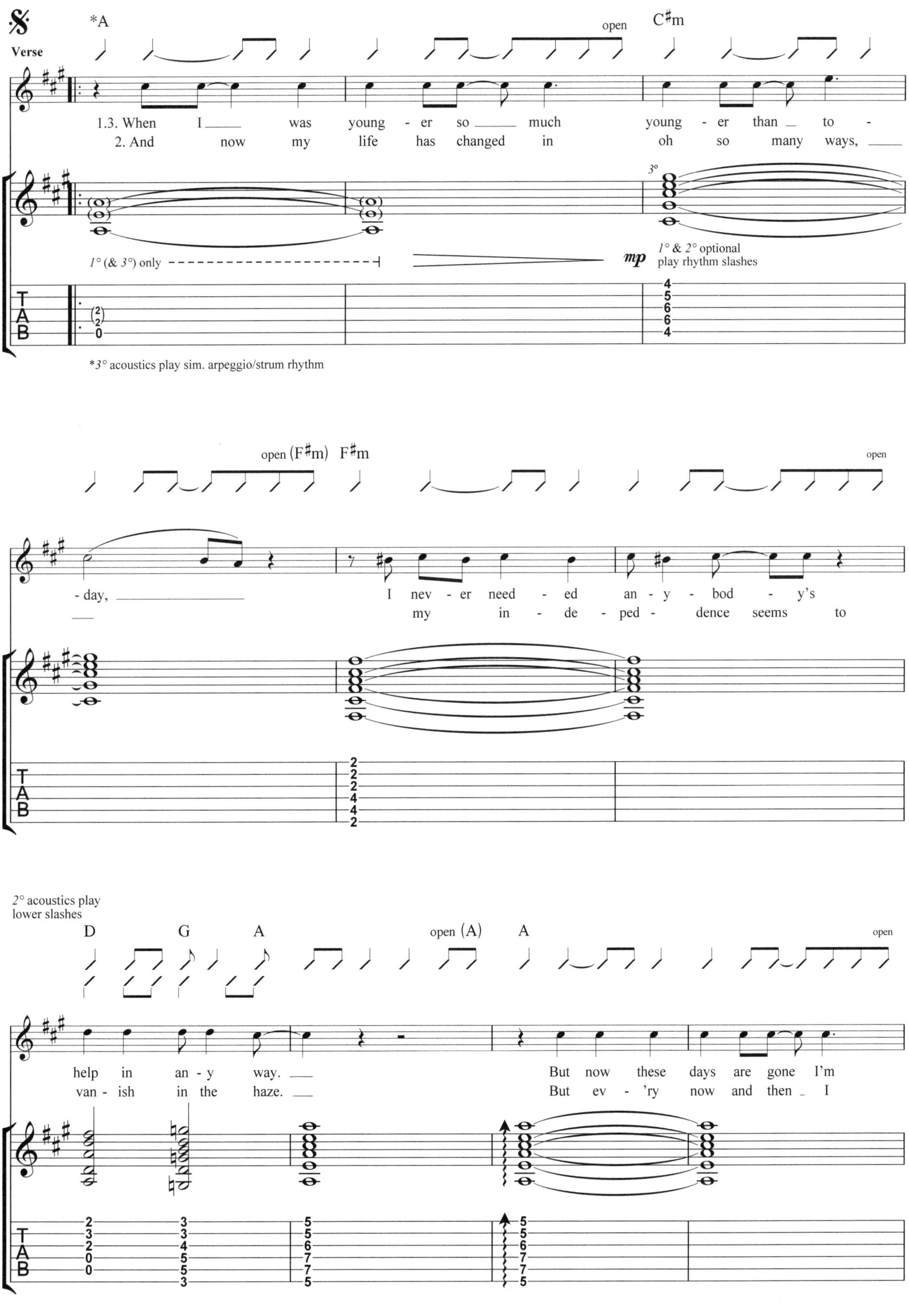
Verse
*A
open
C♯m
1.3. When I was young - er so much young - er than to -
2. And now my life has changed in oh so many ways,
3°
1° (& 3°) only
mp
1° & 2° optional play rhythm slashes
*3° acoustics play sim. arpeggio/strum rhythm
open (F♯m) F♯m
open
- day,
I nev - er need - ed an - y - bod - y's
my in - de - ped - dence seems to
2° acoustics play lower slashes
D G A
open (A) A
open
help in an - y way.
van - ish in the haze.
But now these days are gone I'm
But ev - 'ry now and then I

C♯m
open (F♯m)
F♯m
not so self as - sured,
now I find I've
feel so in - se - cure,
I know that I just
open
D
G
A
2° acoustics play lower slashes
changed my mind,
I've op - ened up the doors.
need you like
I've never done be - fore.
Bm
Chorus
cont. sim.
Help me if you can I'm feel - ing down.
And I do
mf
Gtr. 4 (elec.)
f w/clean tone
*Play Gtrs. 3 & 4 as composite part
G
ap - pre - ci - ate you be - ing round.

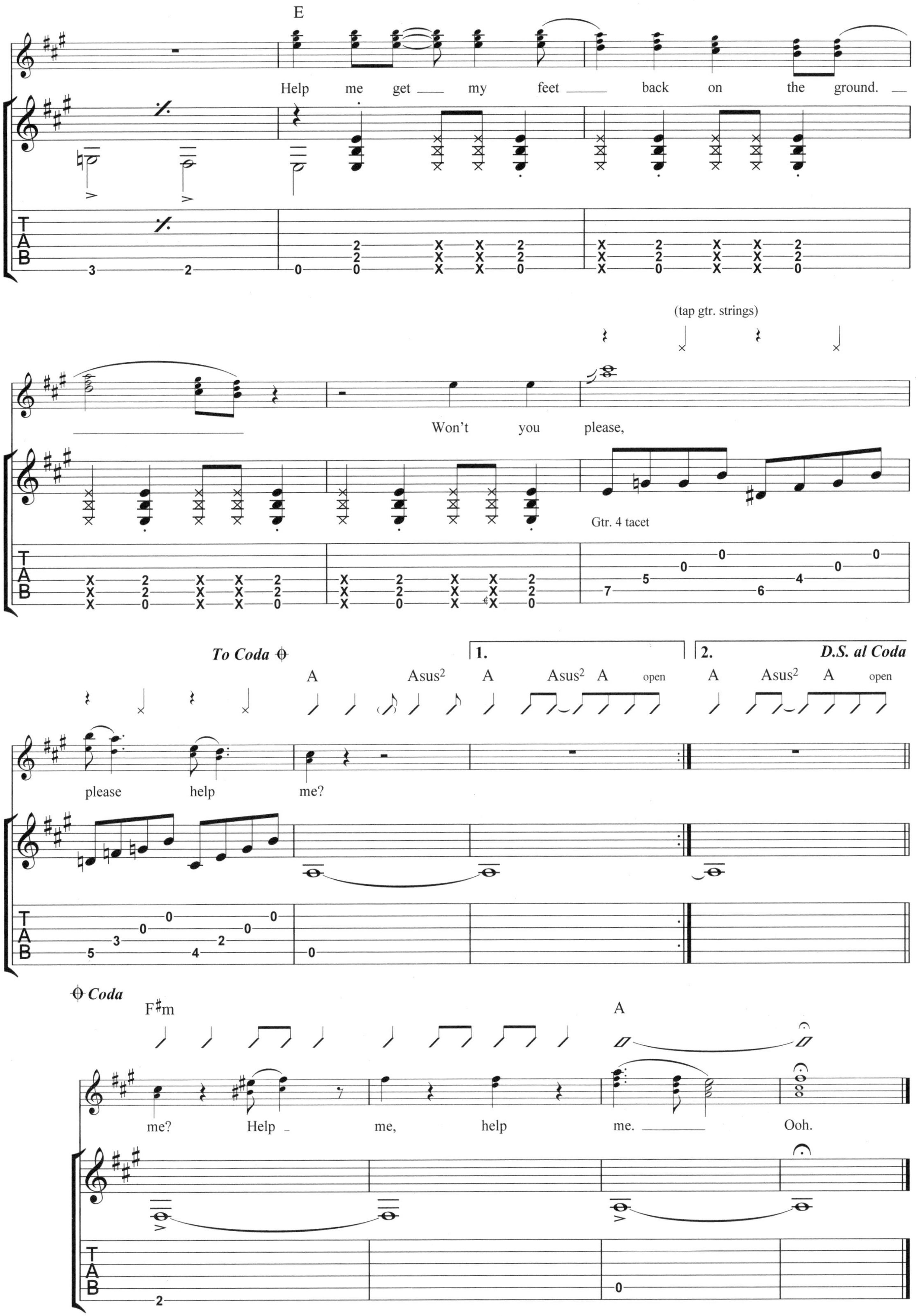
E
Help me get my feet back on the ground.
(tap gtr. strings)
Won't you please,
Gtr. 4 tacet
To Coda
1.
2.
D.S. al Coda
A Asus2 A Asus2 A open
A Asus2 A open
please help me?
Coda
F#m
A
me? Help me, help me. Ooh.

YESTERDAY

Words & Music by John Lennon & Paul McCartney

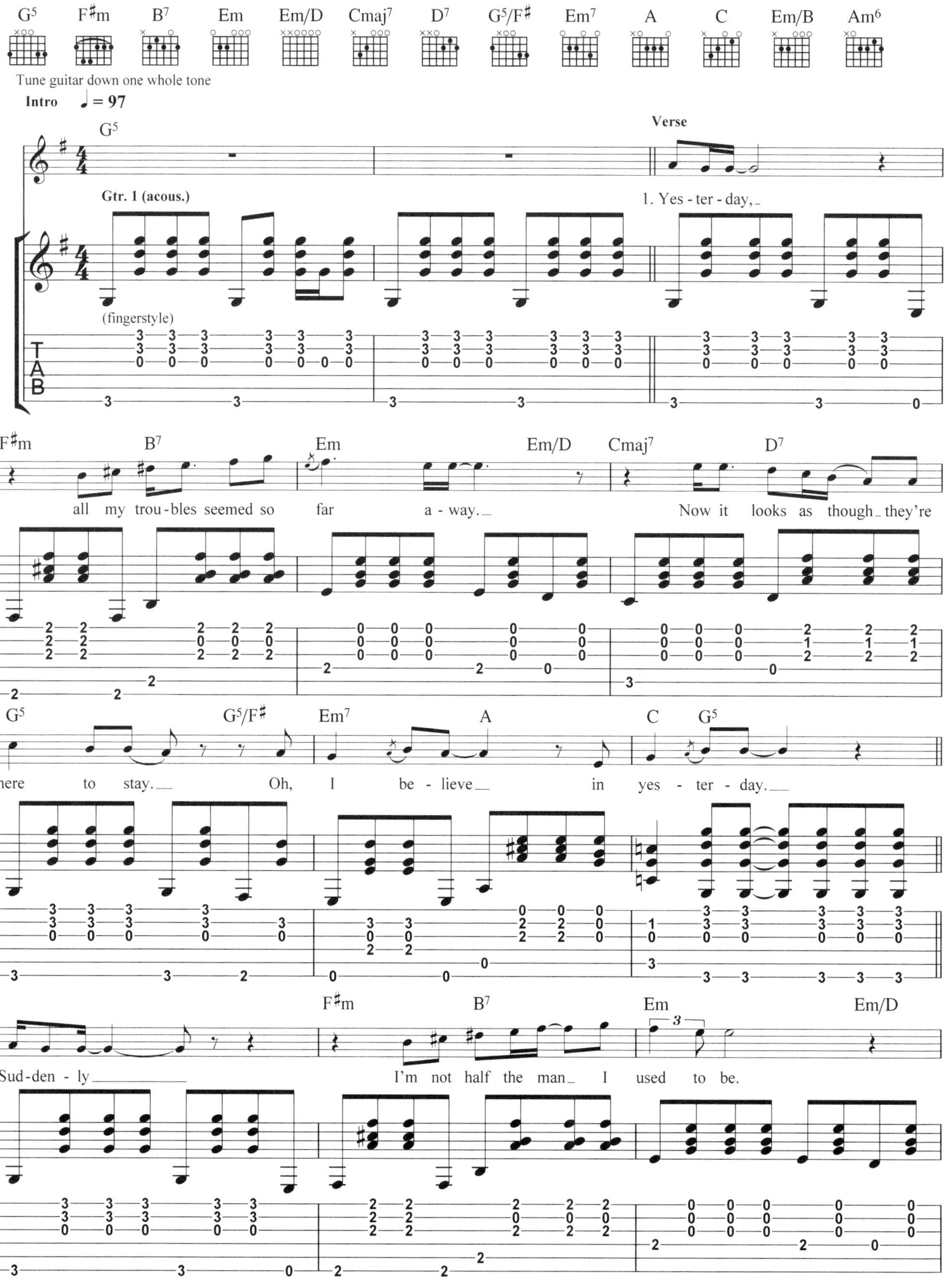

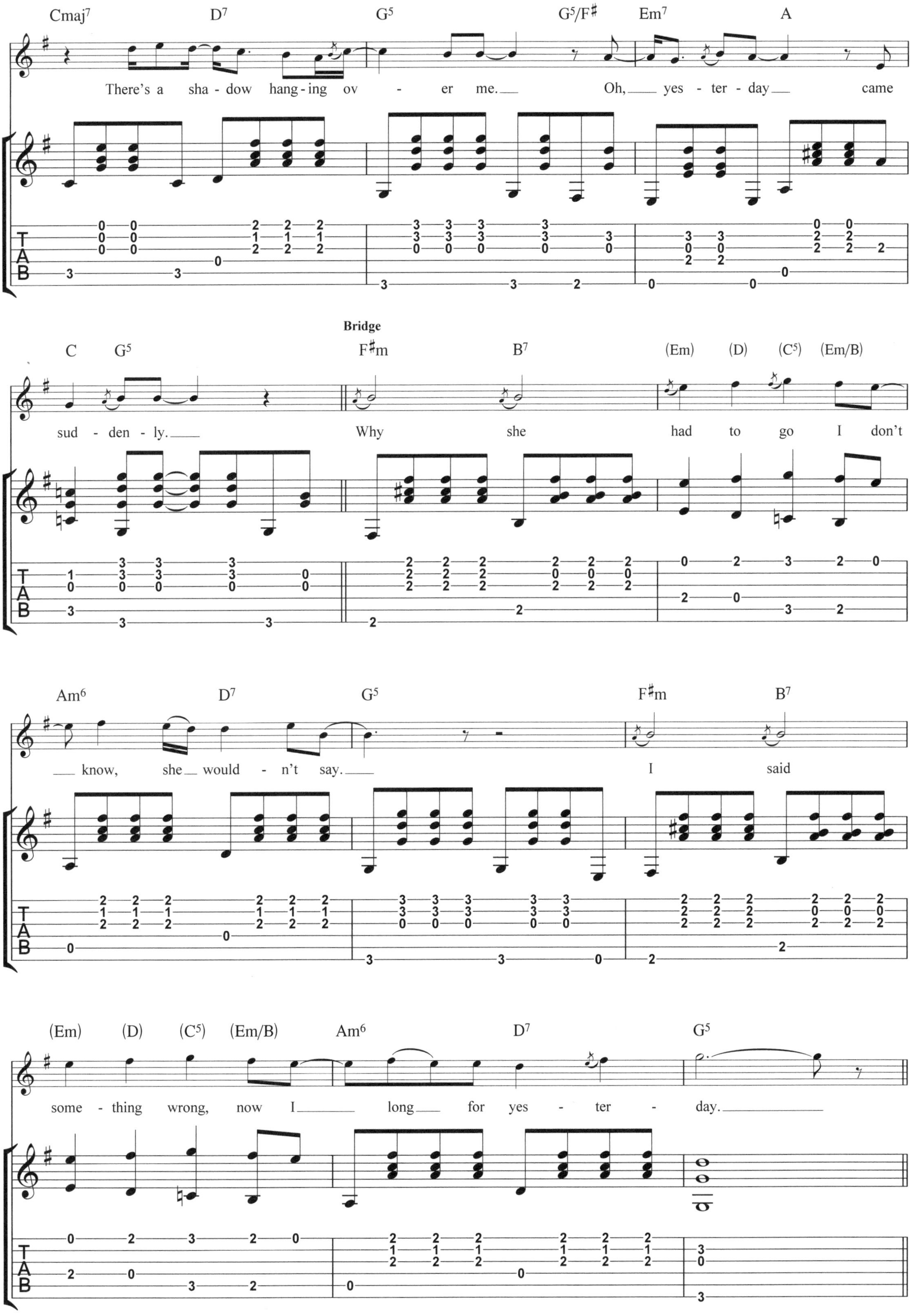
Cmaj7 D7 G5 G5/F# Em7 A
There's a sha - dow hang - ing ov - er me. Oh, yes - ter - day came
Bridge
C G5 F#m B7 (Em) (D) (C5) (Em/B)
sud - den - ly. Why she had to go I don't
Am6 D7 G5 F#m B7
know, she would - n't say. I said
(Em) (D) (C5) (Em/B) Am6 D7 G5
some - thing wrong, now I long for yes - ter - day.
TAB

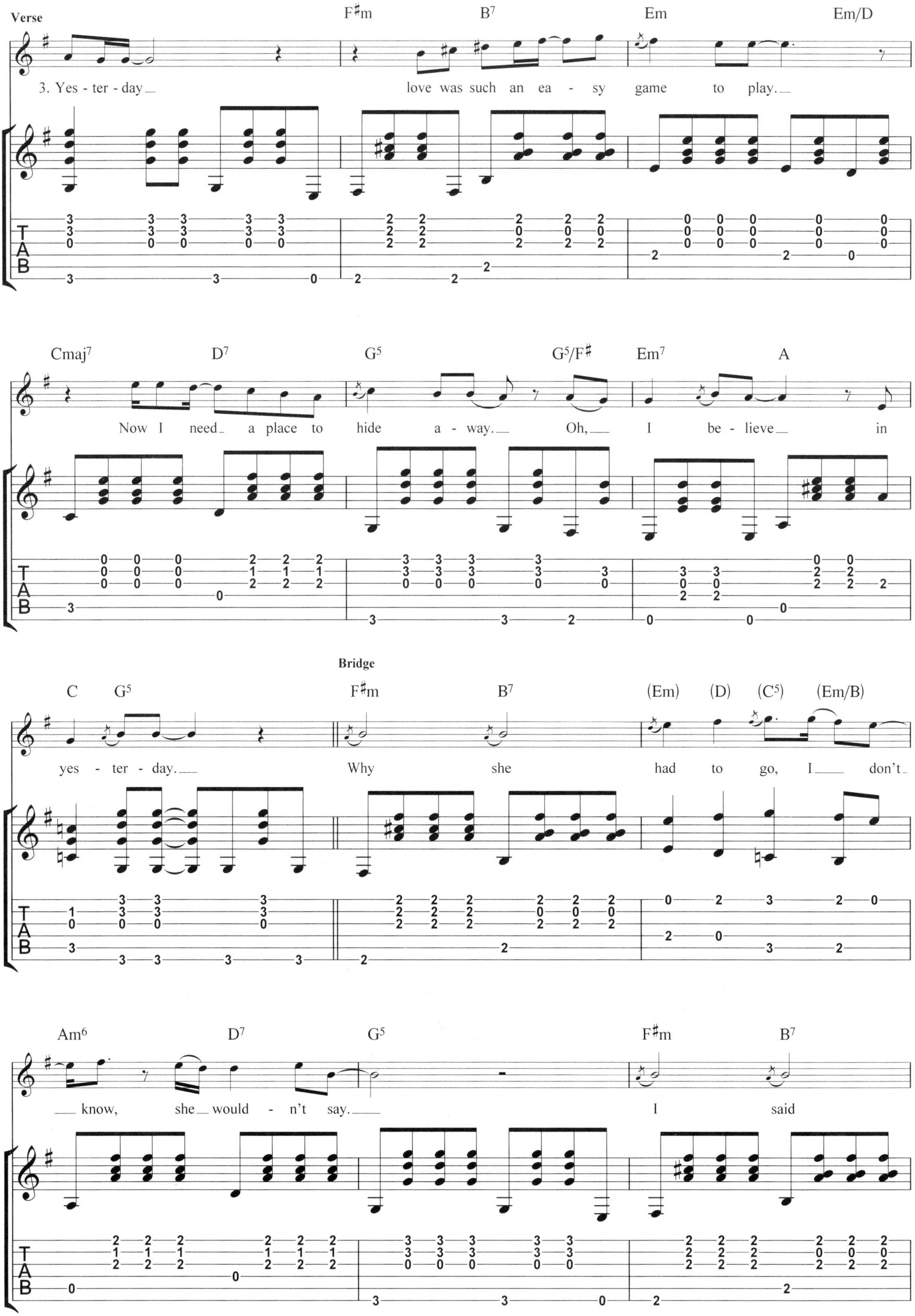
Verse
F♯m B7 Em Em/D
3. Yes - ter - day love was such an ea - sy game to play.
Cmaj7 D7 G5 G5/F♯ Em7 A
Now I need a place to hide a - way. Oh, I be - lieve in
Bridge
C G5 F♯m B7 (Em) (D) (C5) (Em/B)
yes - ter - day. Why she had to go, I don't
Am6 D7 G5 F♯m B7
know, she would - n't say. I said
TAB

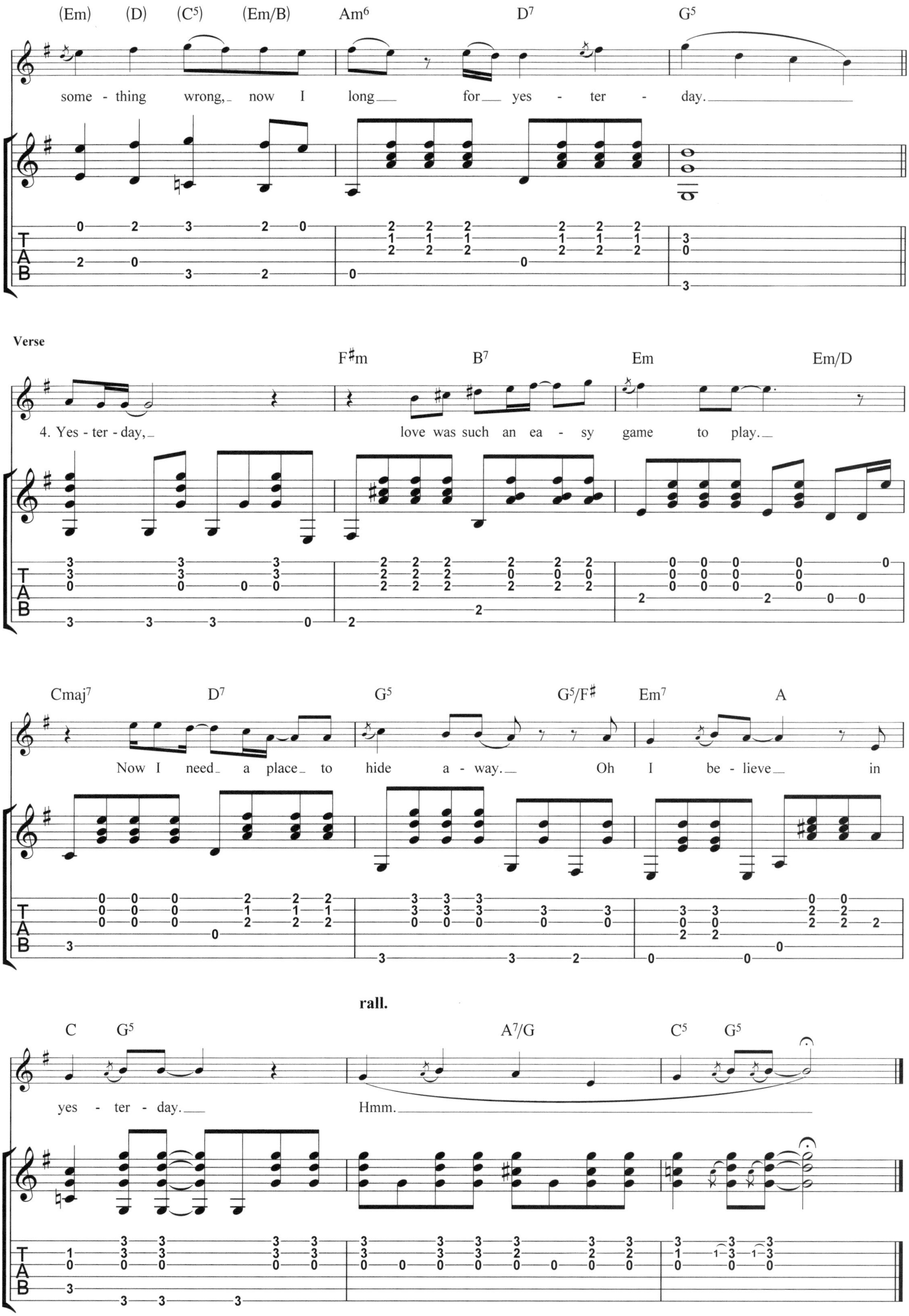
(Em) (D) (C5) (Em/B) Am6 D7 G5
some - thing wrong, now I long for yes - ter - day.
Verse
F♯m B7 Em Em/D
4. Yes - ter - day, love was such an ea - sy game to play.
Cmaj7 D7 G5 G5/F♯ Em7 A
Now I need a place to hide a - way. Oh I be - lieve in
rall.
C G5 A7/G C5 G5
yes - ter - day. Hmm.

YELLOW SUBMARINE

Words & Music by John Lennon & Paul McCartney

*Horns arr. for Gtr. 2

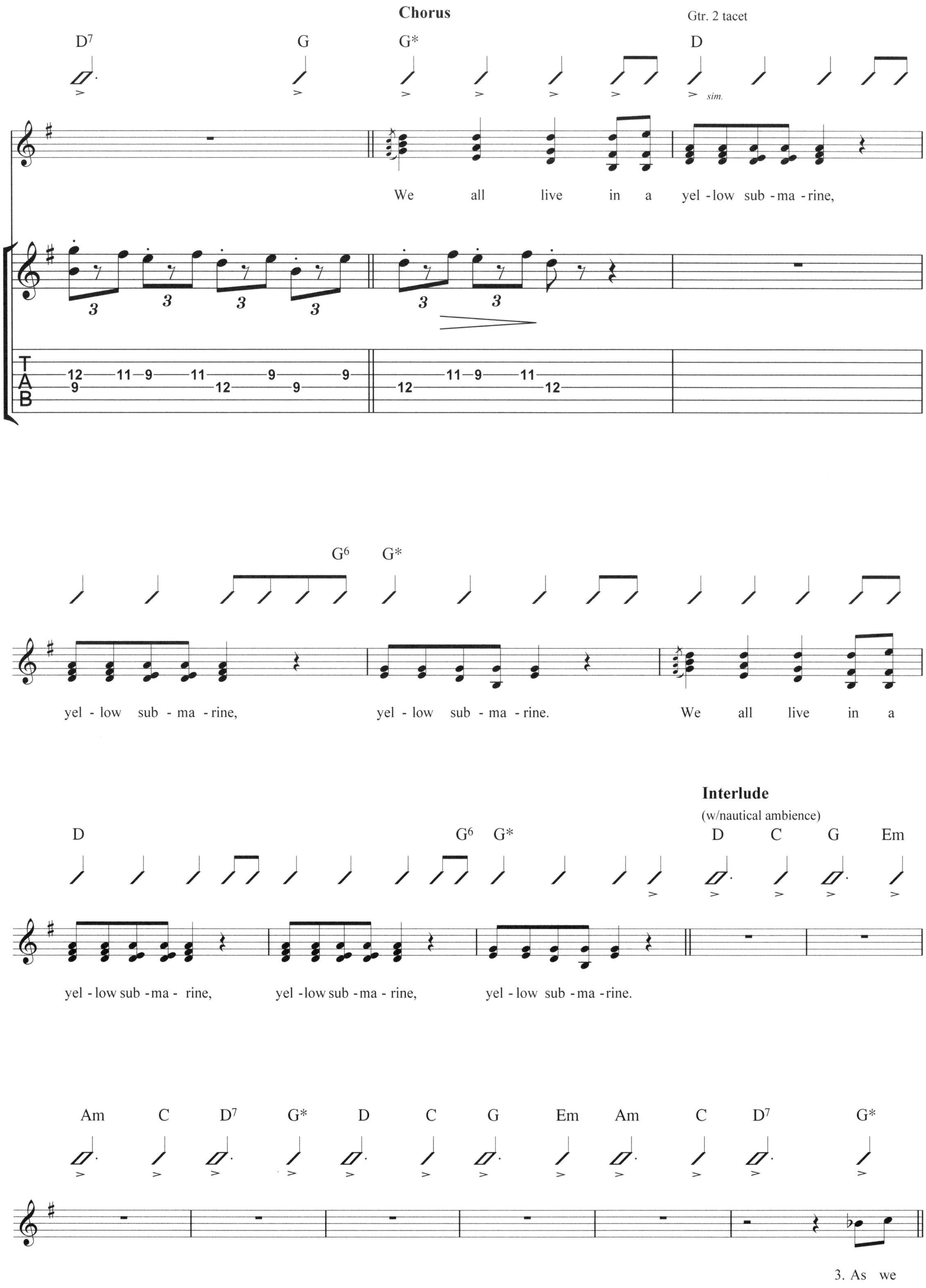
Chorus
Gtr. 2 tacet
D7 G G* D
sim.
We all live in a yel-low sub-ma-rine,
G6 G*
yel-low sub-ma-rine, yel-low sub-ma-rine. We all live in a
Interlude
(w/nautical ambience)
D G6 G* D C G Em
yel-low sub-ma-rine, yel-low sub-ma-rine, yel-low sub-ma-rine.
Am C D7 G* D C G Em Am C D7 G*
3. As we

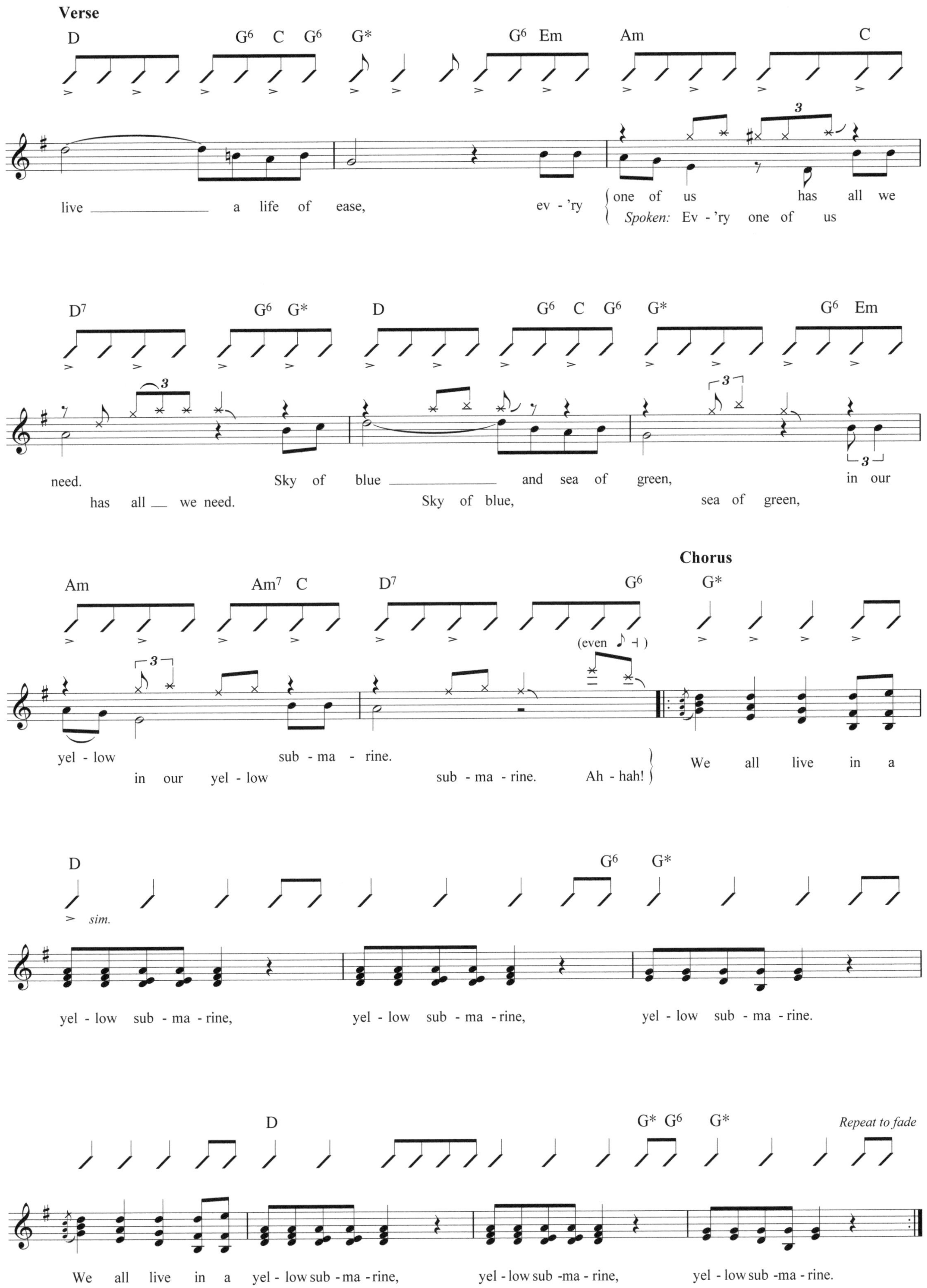
Verse
D G6 C G6 G* G6 Em Am C
live a life of ease, ev - 'ry one of us has all we
Spoken: Ev - 'ry one of us
D7 G6 G* D G6 C G6 G* G6 Em
need. Sky of blue and sea of green, in our
has all we need. Sky of blue, sea of green,
Chorus
Am Am7 C D7 G6 G*
(even)
yel - low sub - ma - rine.
in our yel - low sub - ma - rine. Ah - hah!
We all live in a
D G6 G*
sim.
yel - low sub - ma - rine, yel - low sub - ma - rine, yel - low sub - ma - rine.
D G* G6 G*
Repeat to fade
We all live in a yel - low sub - ma - rine, yel - low sub - ma - rine, yel - low sub - ma - rine.

DAY TRIPPER

Words & Music by John Lennon & Paul McCartney

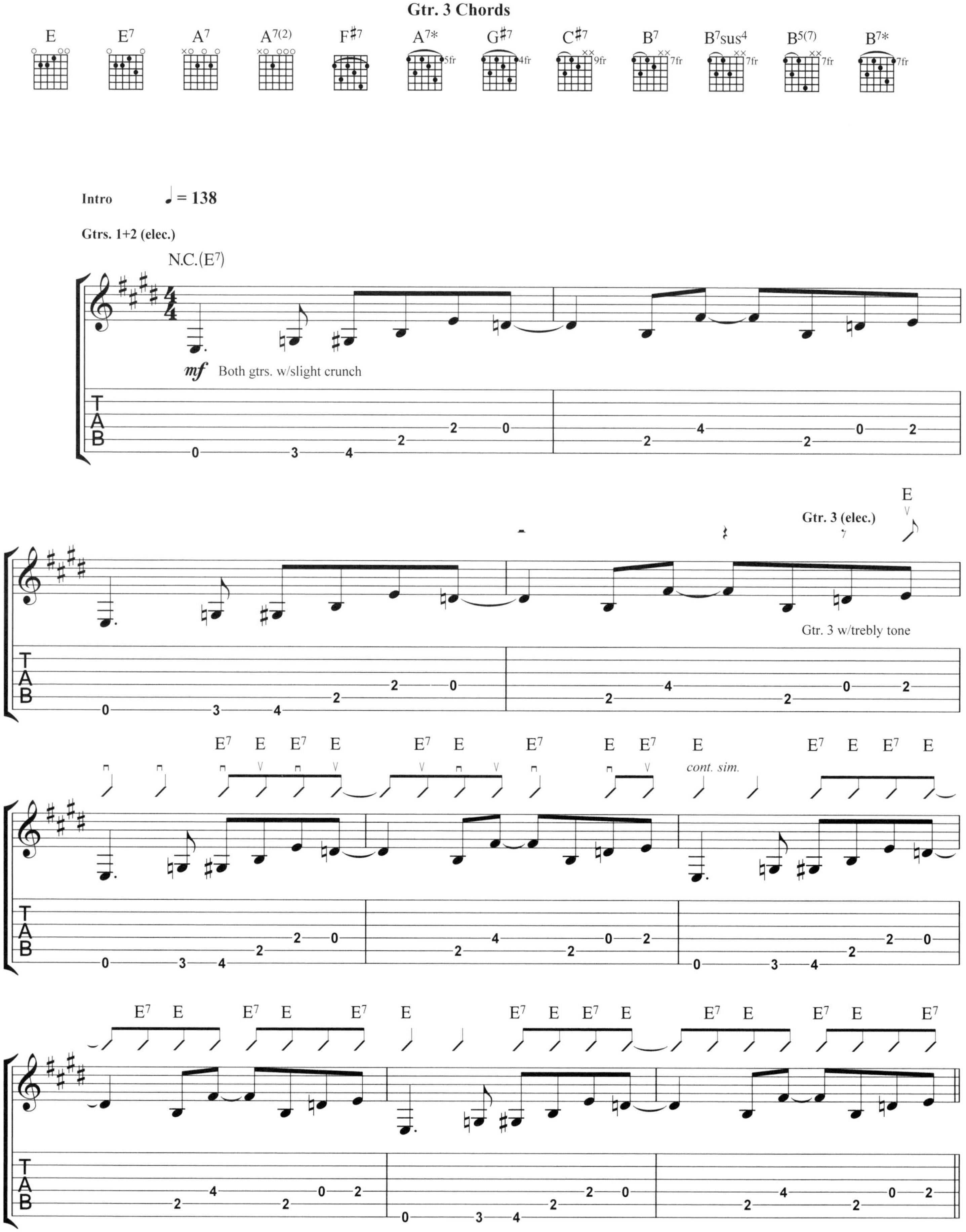

Verse
E E7 E E7 E E7 E E7 E E7 E E7 E E7 E
1. Got a good rea - son for tak - ing the ea - sy way out.
2. She's a big tea - ser, she took me half the way there.
3. Tried to please her, she on - ly played one - night stands.
E7 E E7 E open A7 A7(2) A7 A7(2) A7 A7(2) A7 A7(2) A7
Got a good rea - son for
She's a big teas - er,
Tried to please her,
E E7 E E7 E E7 E E7 E open
tak - ing the ea - sy way out, now.
she took me half the way there, now.
she on - ly played one night stands, now.
She was a

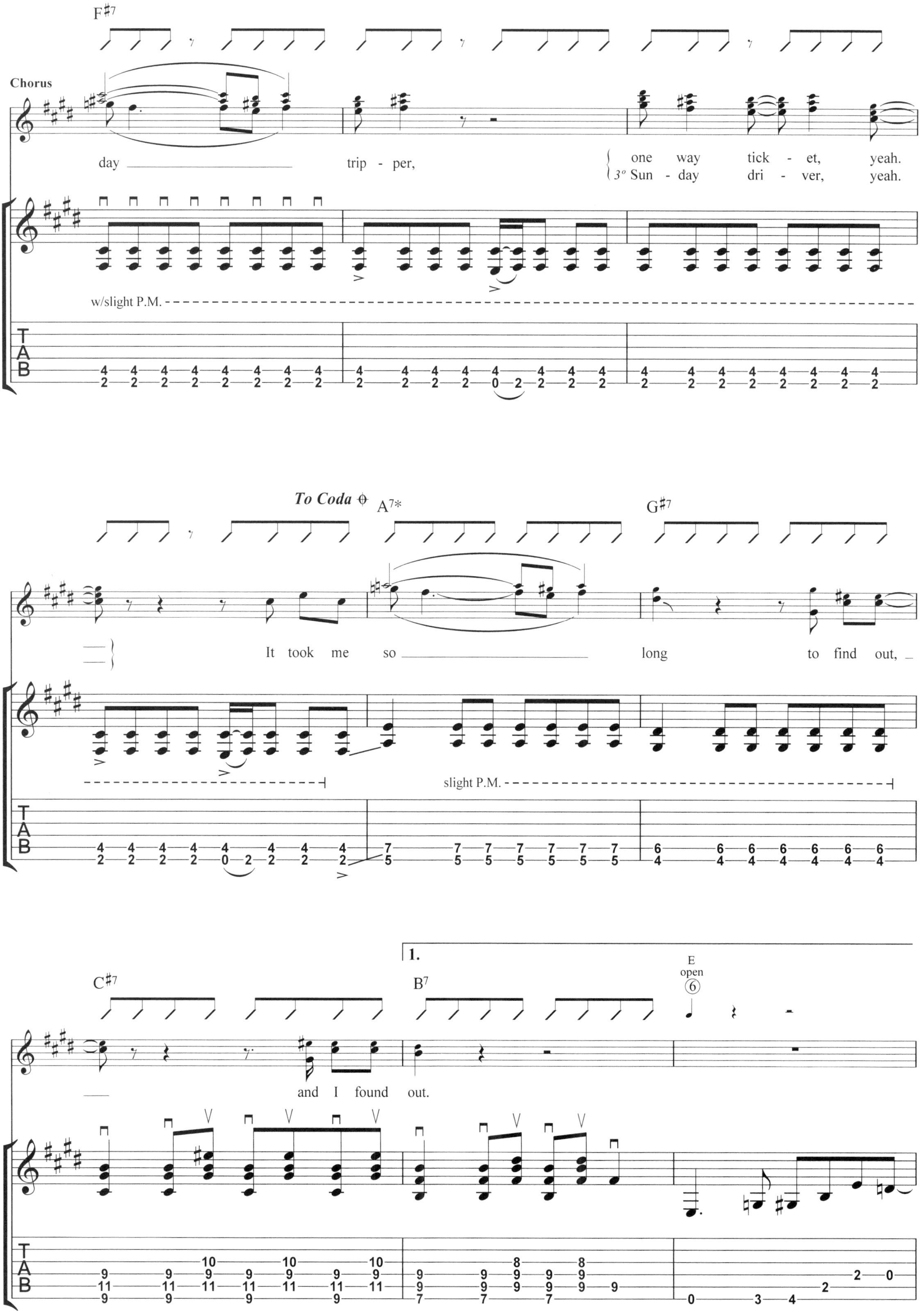
F♯7
Chorus
day trip - per,
one way tick - et, yeah.
3° Sun - day dri - ver, yeah.
w/slight P.M.
To Coda
A7*
G♯7
It took me so long to find out,
slight P.M.
C♯7
1.
B7
E open 6
and I found out.

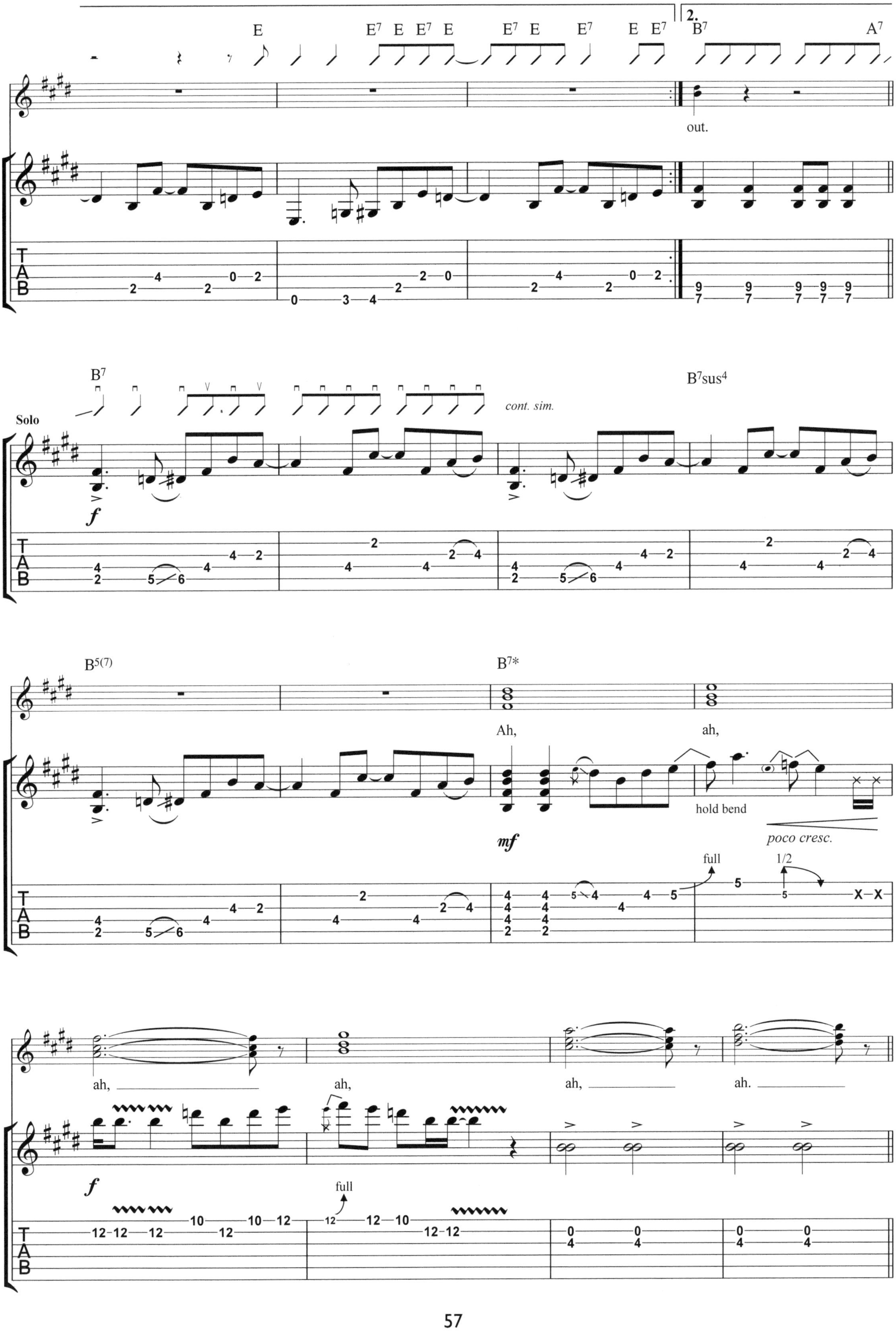
E
E7 E E7 E
E7 E
E7
E E7
2.
B7
A7
out.
Solo
B7
cont. sim.
B7sus4
B5(7)
B7*
Ah,
ah,
hold bend
poco cresc.
full
1/2
ah,
ah,
ah,
ah.
full

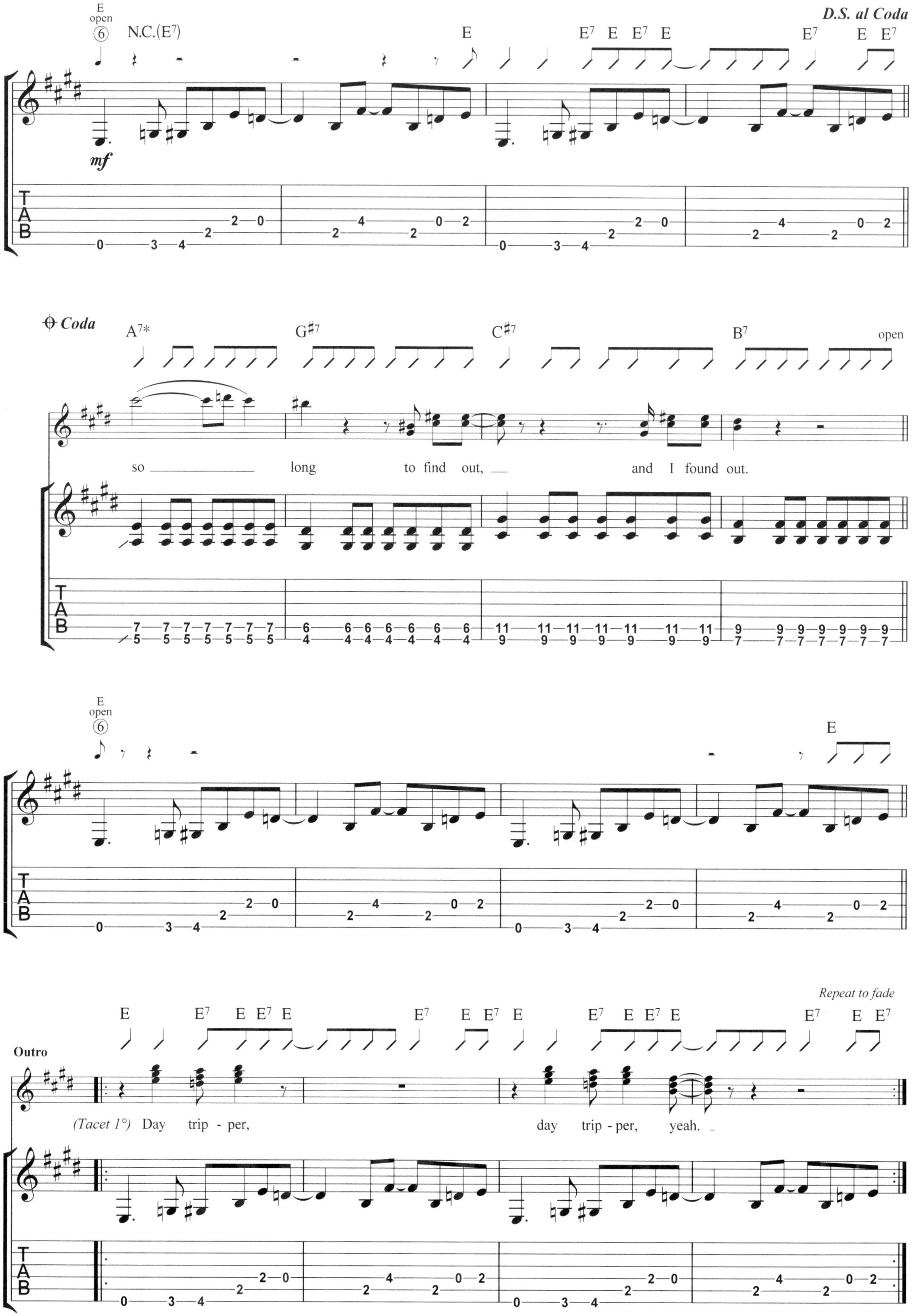
D.S. al Coda
E open 6
N.C.(E7)
E
E7 E E7 E
E7 E E7
mf
Coda
A7*
G#7
C#7
B7
open
so long to find out, and I found out.
E open 6
E
Repeat to fade
Outro
E E7 E E7 E E7 E E7 E E7 E E7 E E7 E E7
(Tacet 1°) Day trip - per, day trip - per, yeah.

WE CAN WORK IT OUT

Words & Music by John Lennon & Paul McCartney

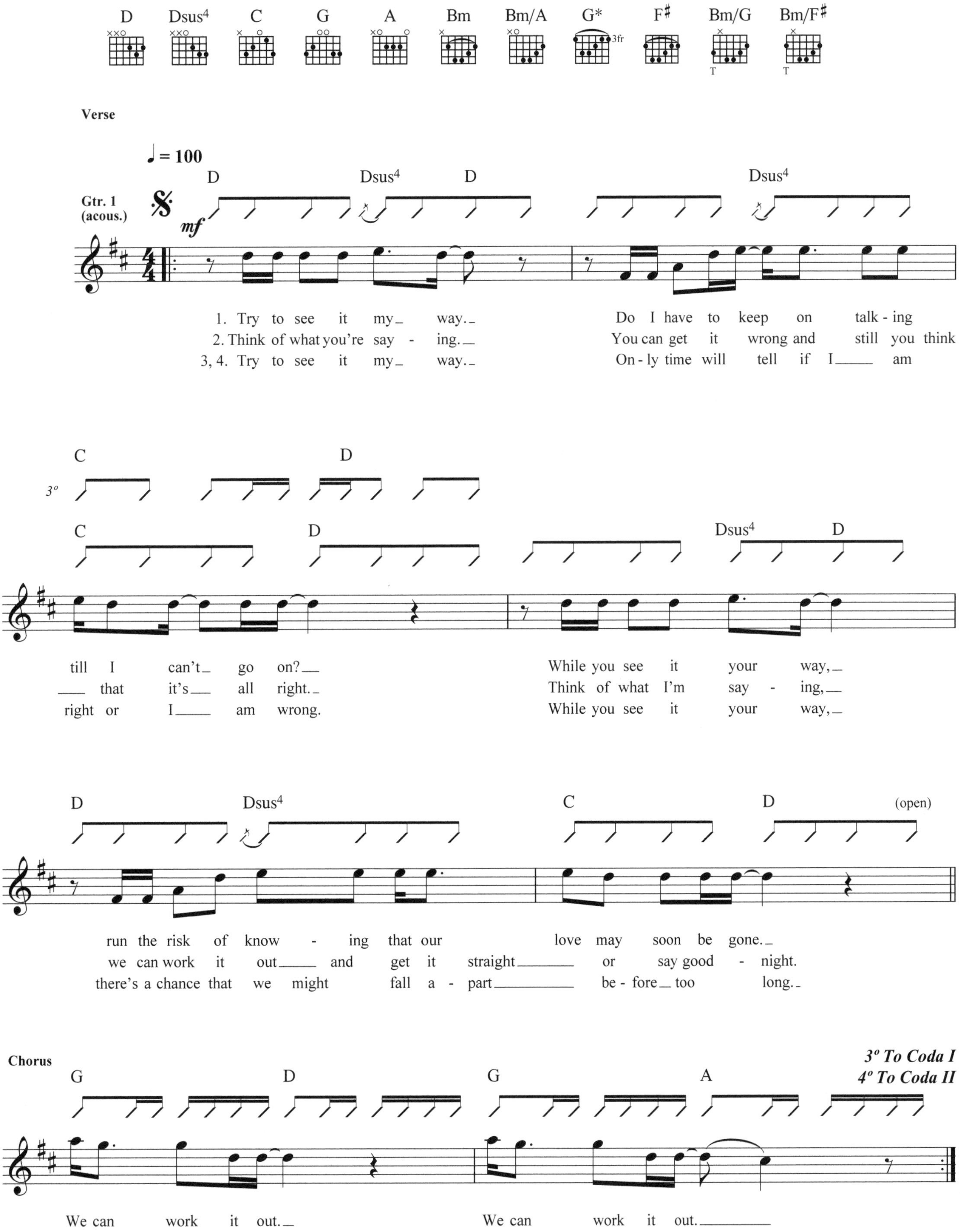

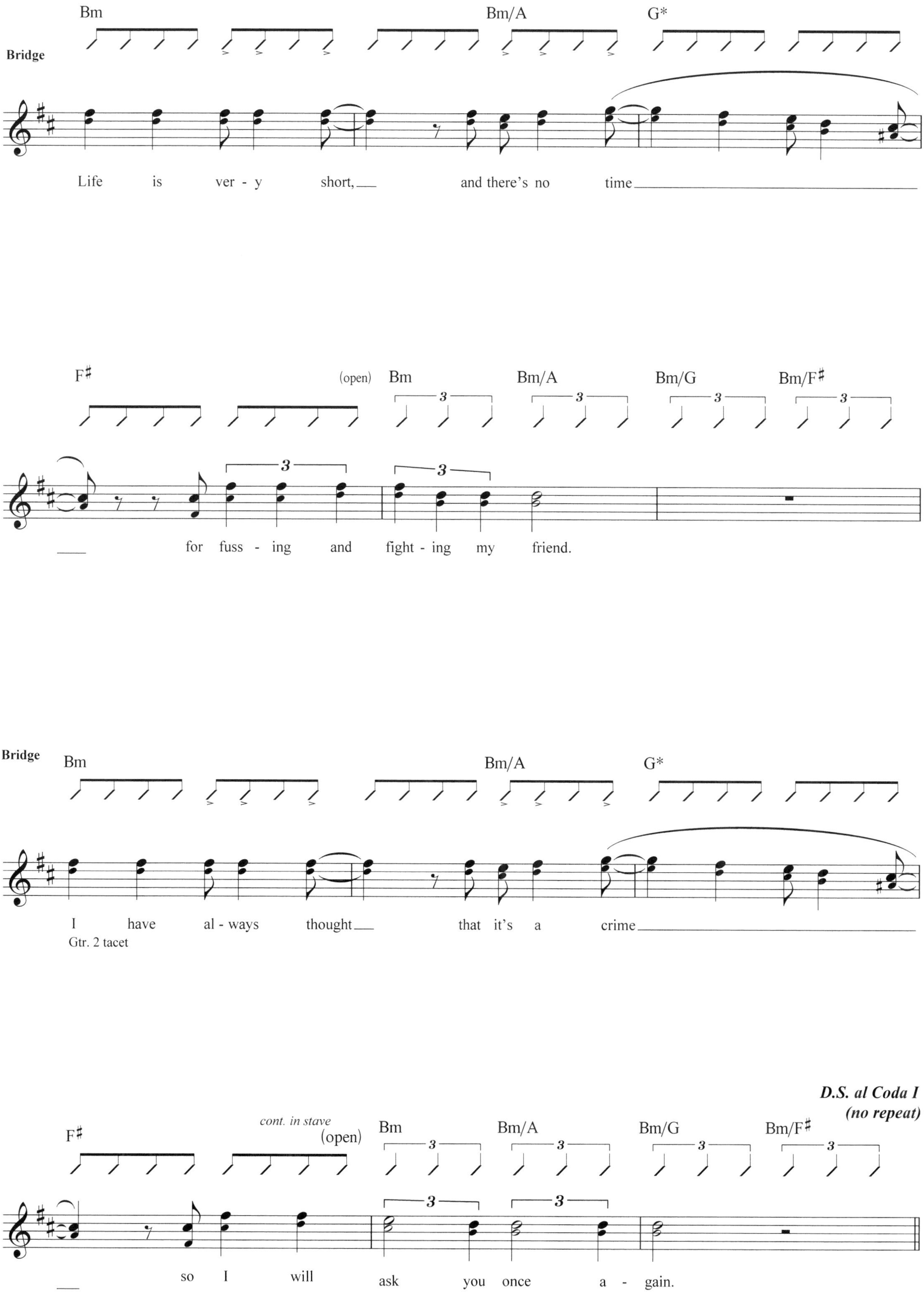
Bridge
Bm
Bm/A
G*
Life is ver - y short, and there's no time
F♯
(open)
Bm
Bm/A
Bm/G
Bm/F♯
for fuss - ing and fight - ing my friend.
Bridge
Bm
Bm/A
G*
I have al - ways thought that it's a crime
Gtr. 2 tacet
D.S. al Coda I
(no repeat)
F♯
cont. in stave
(open)
Bm
Bm/A
Bm/G
Bm/F♯
so I will ask you once a - gain.

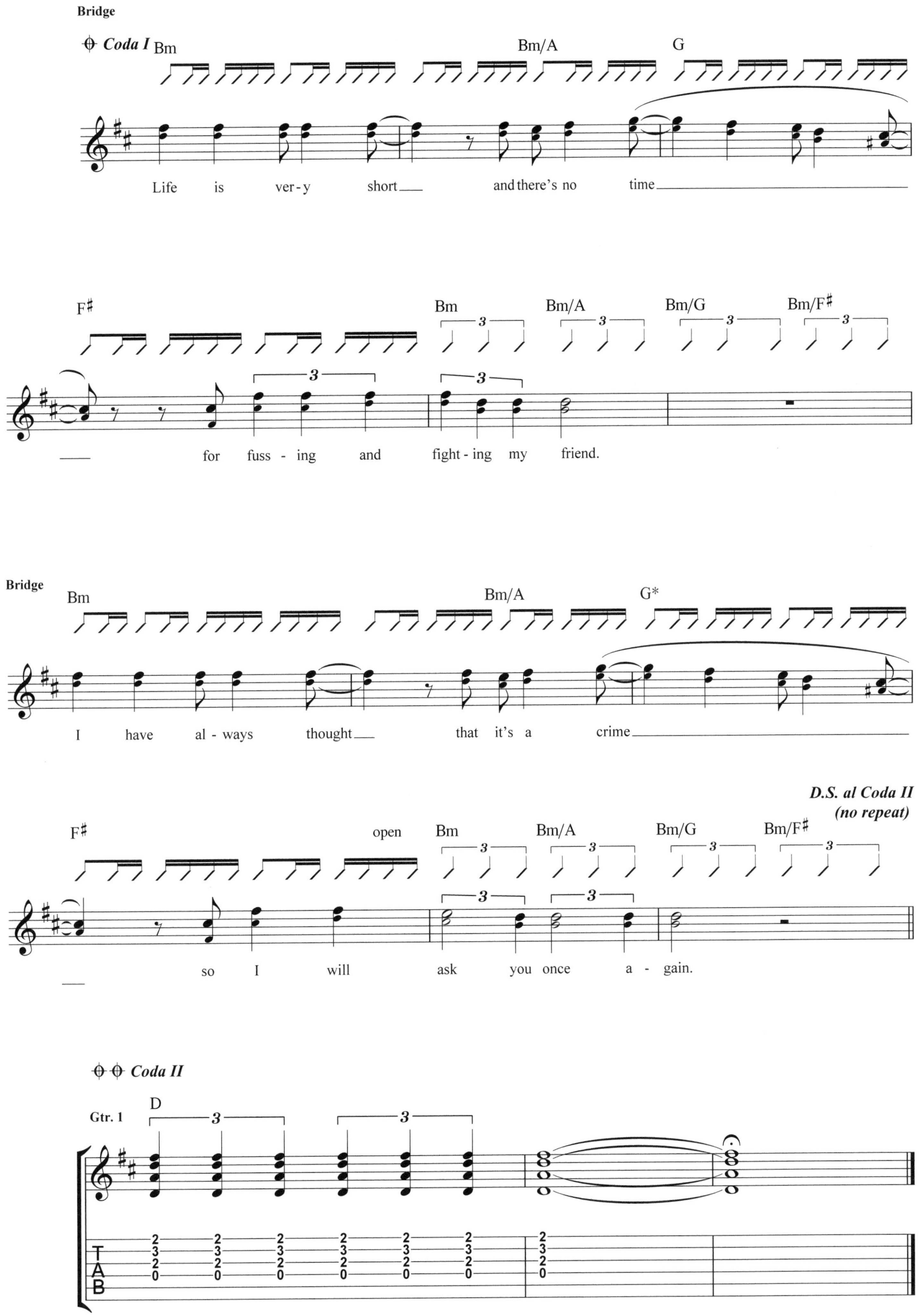
Bridge
Coda I
Bm Bm/A G
Life is ver-y short and there's no time
F♯ Bm Bm/A Bm/G Bm/F♯
for fuss-ing and fight-ing my friend.
Bridge
Bm Bm/A G*
I have al-ways thought that it's a crime
D.S. al Coda II
(no repeat)
F♯ open Bm Bm/A Bm/G Bm/F♯
so I will ask you once a-gain.
Coda II
Gtr. 1
D

PAPERBACK WRITER

Words & Music by John Lennon & Paul McCartney

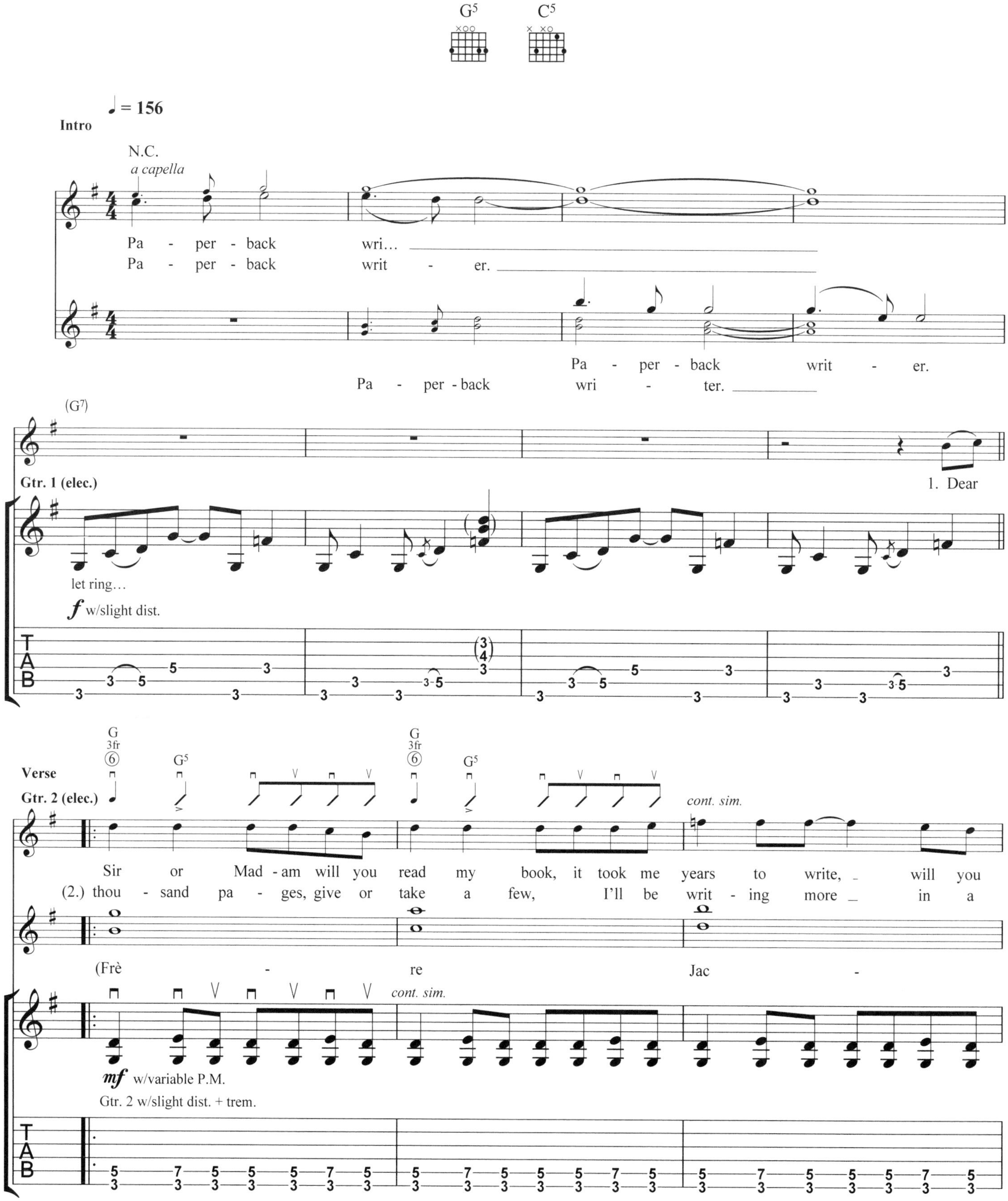

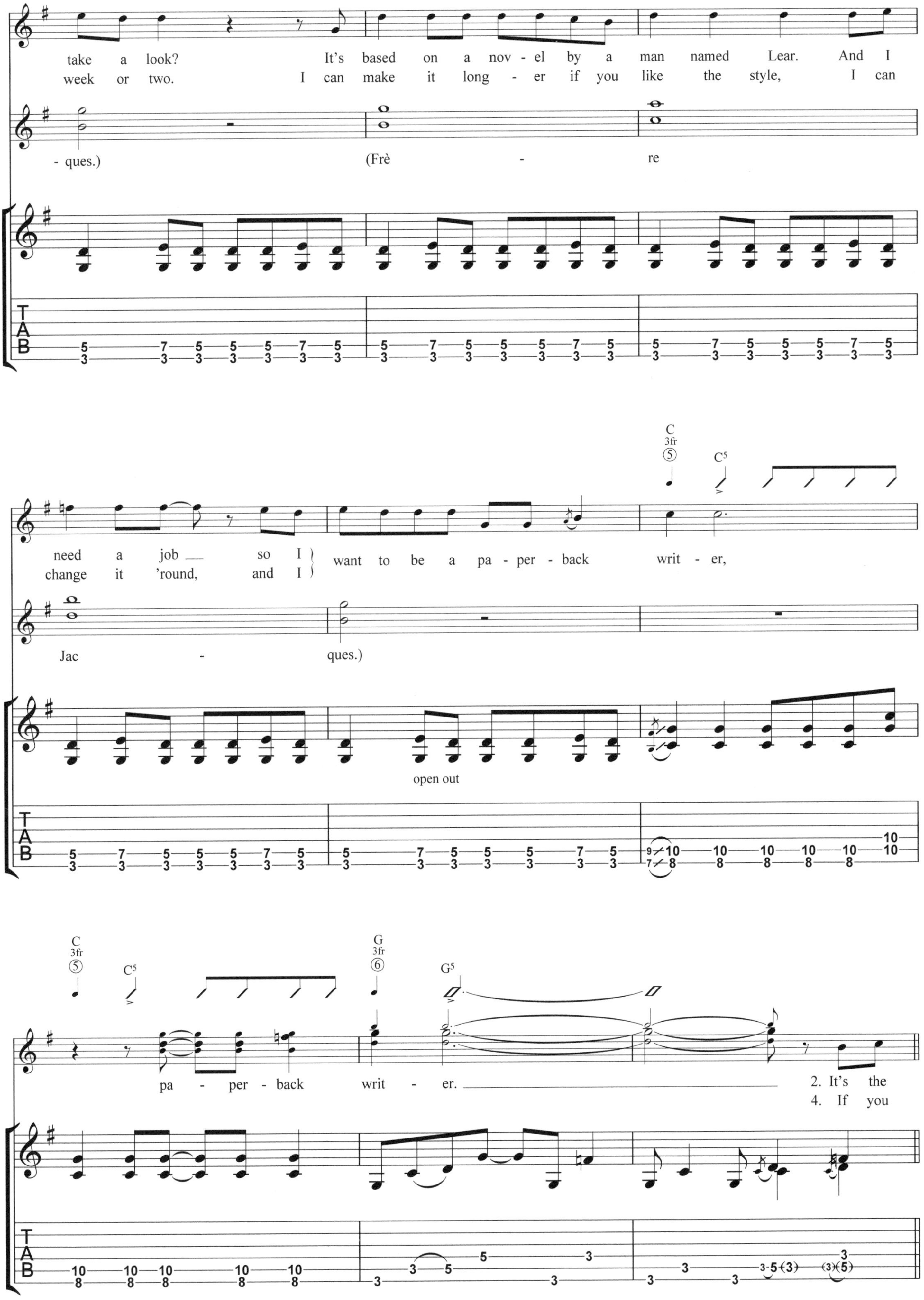
take a look? It's based on a nov - el by a man named Lear. And I
week or two. I can make it long - er if you like the style, I can
- ques.) (Frè - re
T A B
C 3fr ⑤ C5
need a job so I } want to be a pa - per - back writ - er,
change it 'round, and I }
Jac - ques.)
open out
C 3fr ⑤ C5 G 3fr ⑥ G5
pa - per - back writ - er.
2. It's the
4. If you

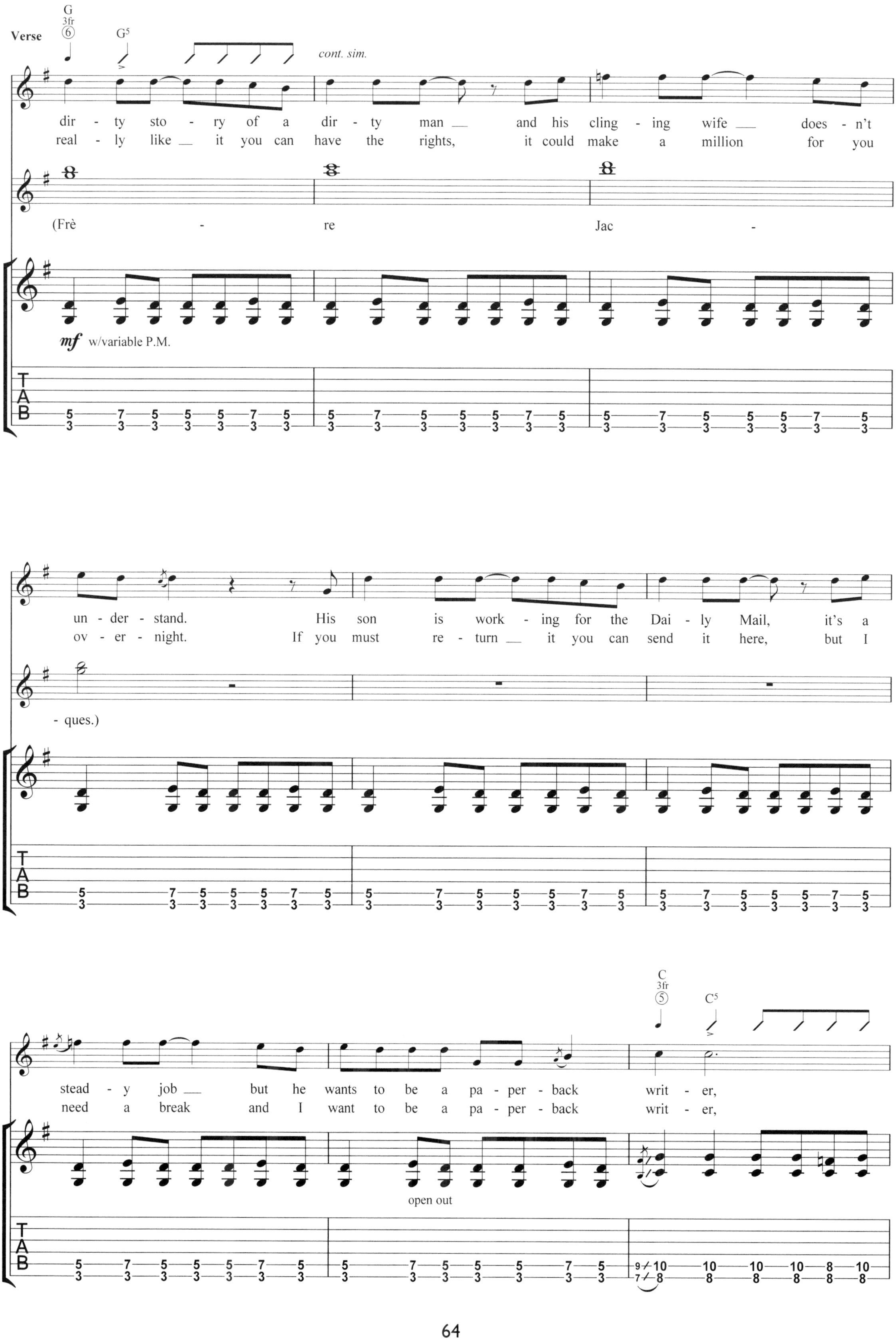
Verse
G 3fr ⑥
G5
cont. sim.
dir - ty sto - ry of a dir - ty man and his cling - ing wife does - n't
real - ly like it you can have the rights, it could make a million for you
(Frè - re Jac -
mf w/variable P.M.
un - der - stand. His son is work - ing for the Dai - ly Mail, it's a
ov - er - night. If you must re - turn it you can send it here, but I
- ques.)
C 3fr ⑤
C5
stead - y job but he wants to be a pa - per - back writ - er,
need a break and I want to be a pa - per - back writ - er,
open out
TAB

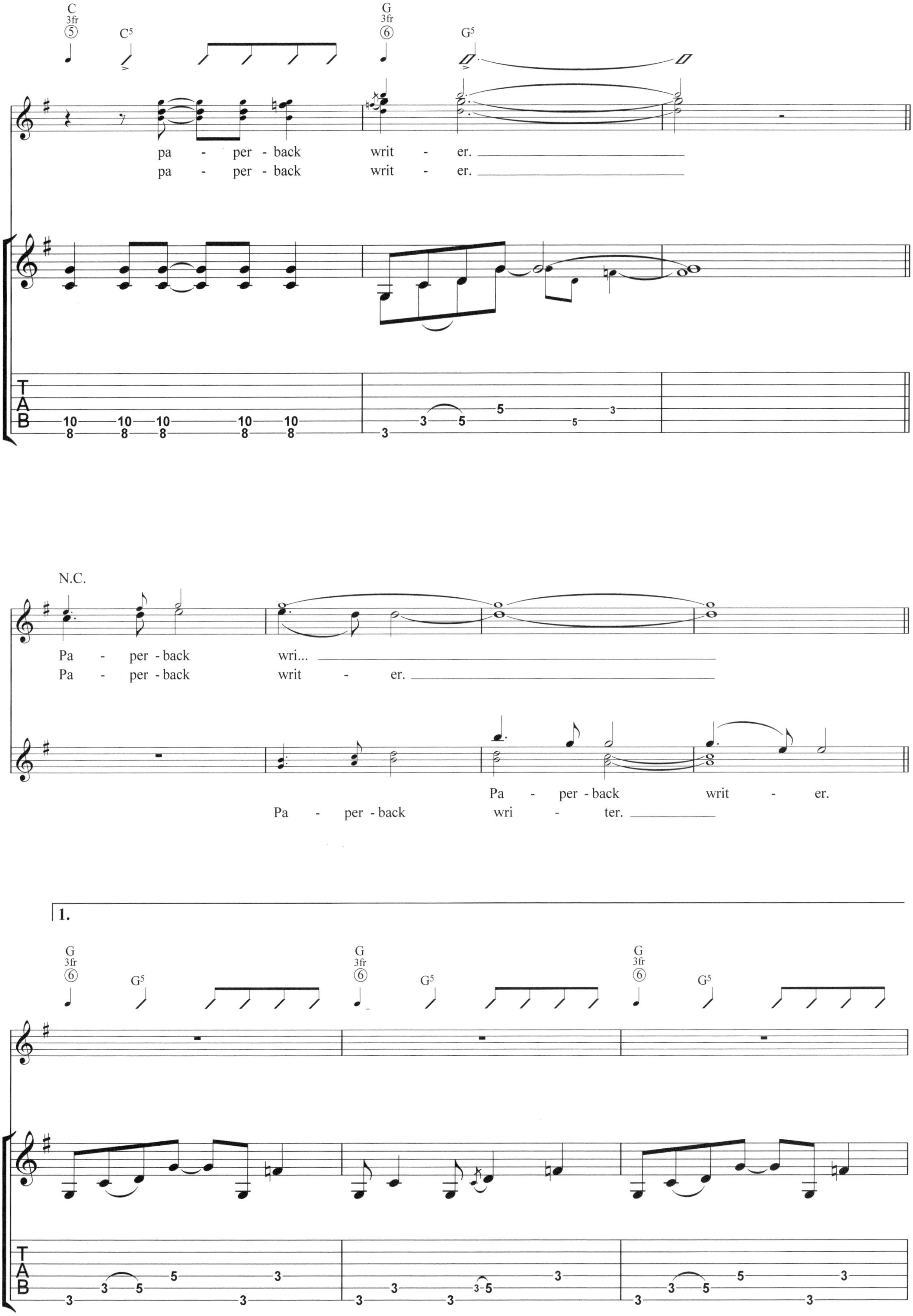
C 3fr ⑤
C5
G 3fr ⑥
G5
pa - per - back writ - er.
pa - per - back writ - er.
N.C.
Pa - per - back wri...
Pa - per - back writ - er.
Pa - per - back writ - er.
Pa - per - back wri - ter.
1.
G 3fr ⑥
G5
G 3fr ⑥
G5
G 3fr ⑥
G5

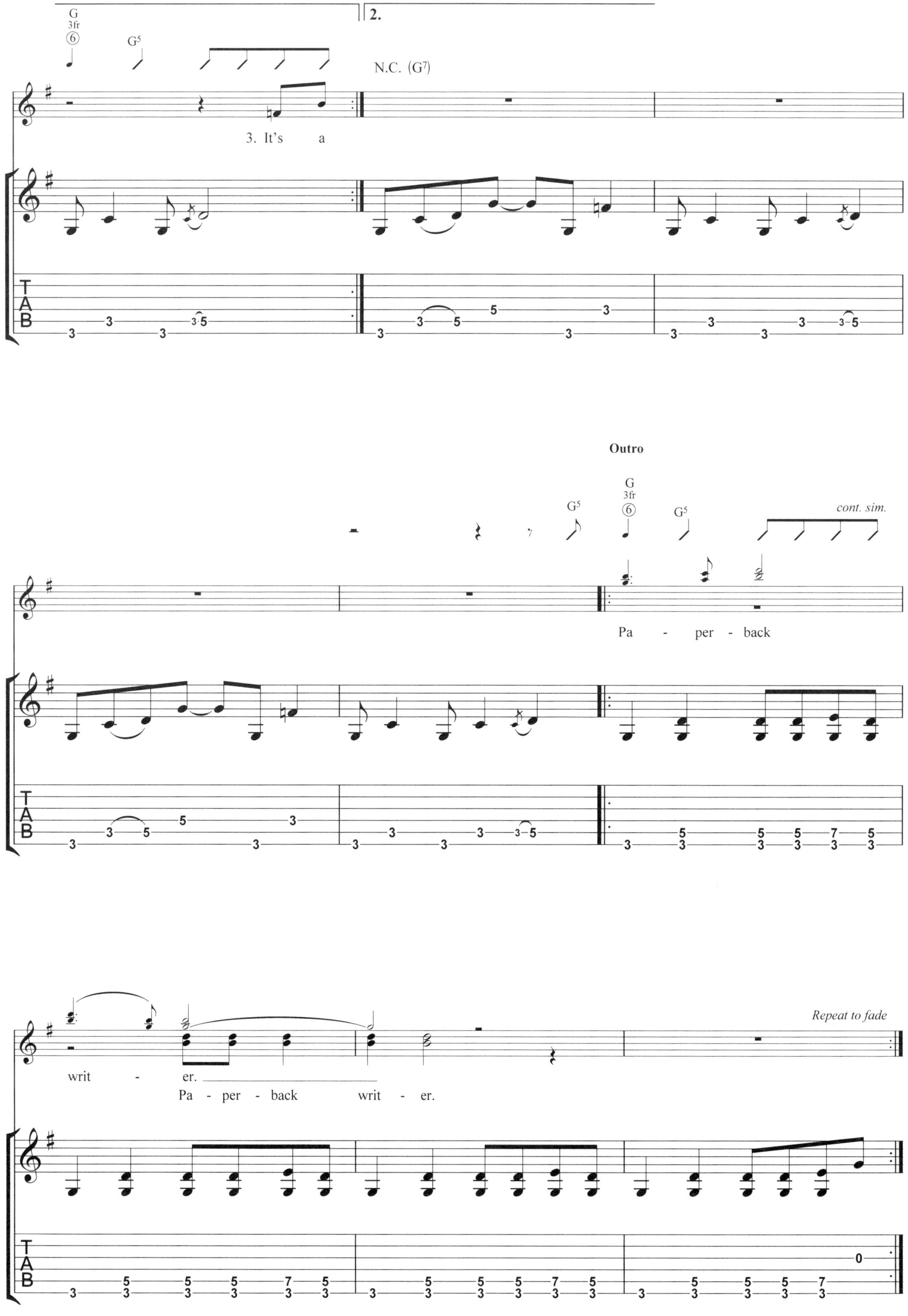
G
3fr
⑥
G5
2.
N.C. (G7)
3. It's a
Outro
G5
G
3fr
⑥
G5
cont. sim.
Pa - per - back
writ - er.
Pa - per - back writ - er.
Repeat to fade

ELEANOR RIGBY

Words & Music by John Lennon & Paul McCartney

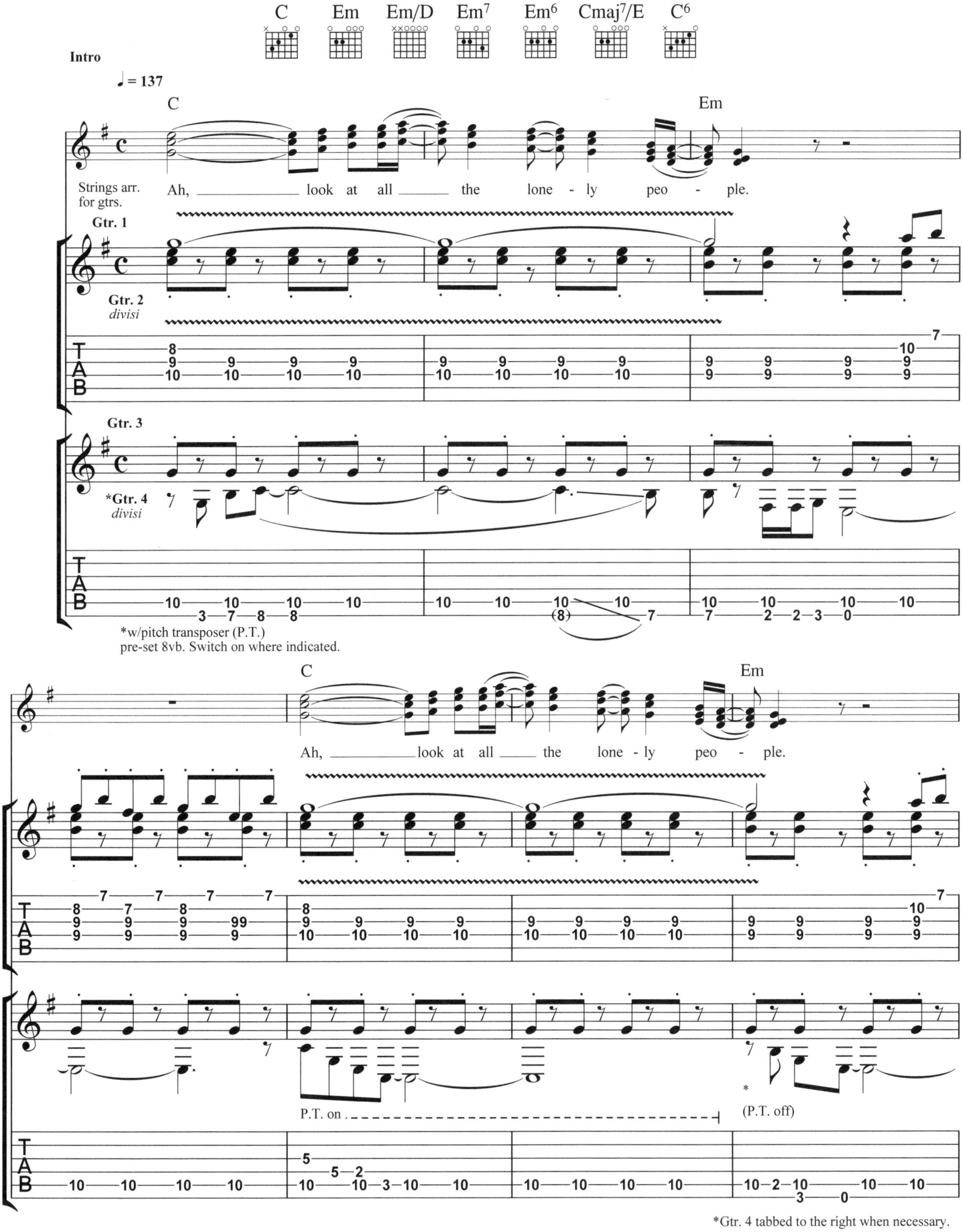

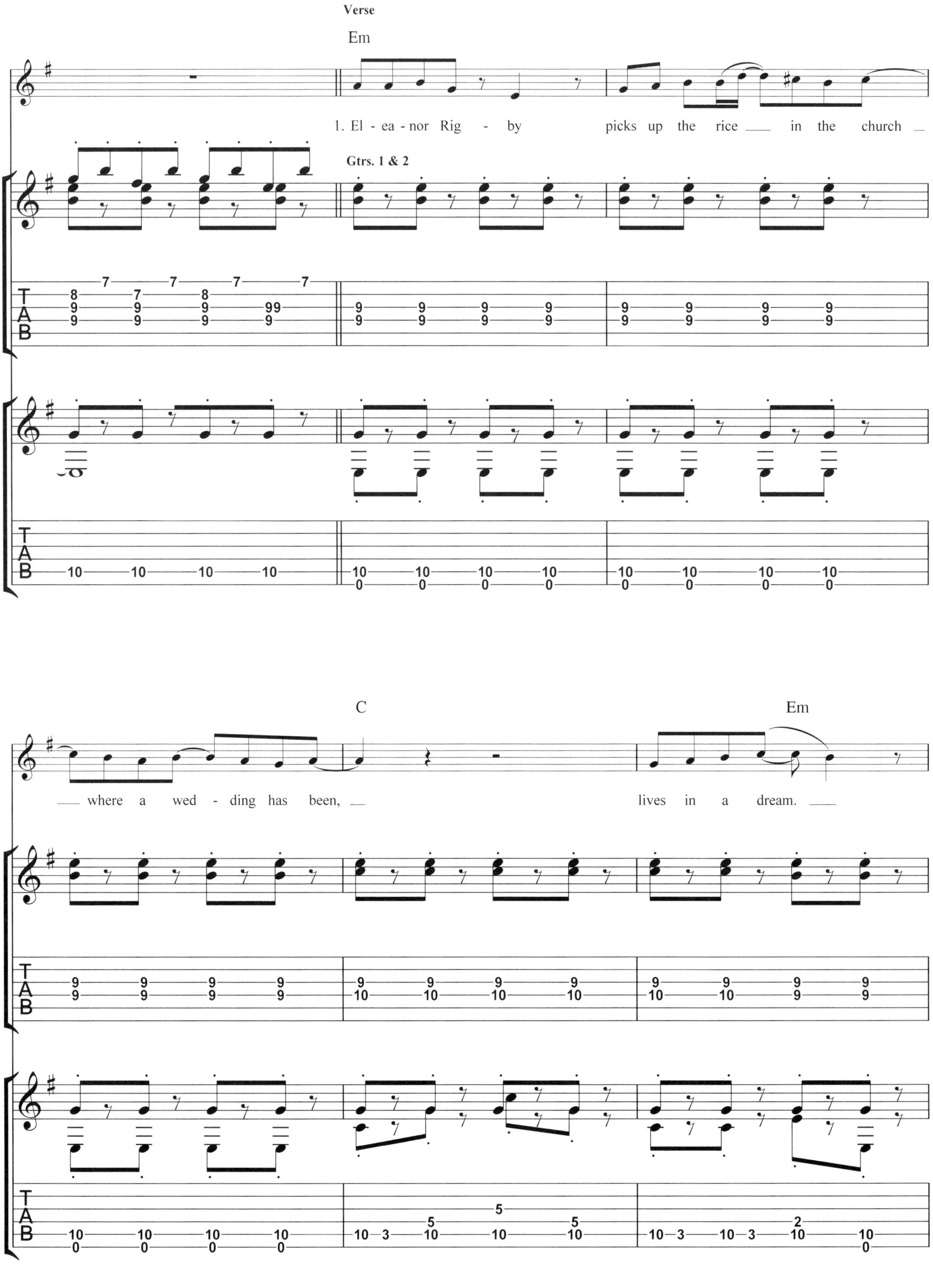
Verse
Em
1. El - ea - nor Rig - by picks up the rice in the church
Gtrs. 1 & 2
C
Em
where a wed - ding has been,
lives in a dream.

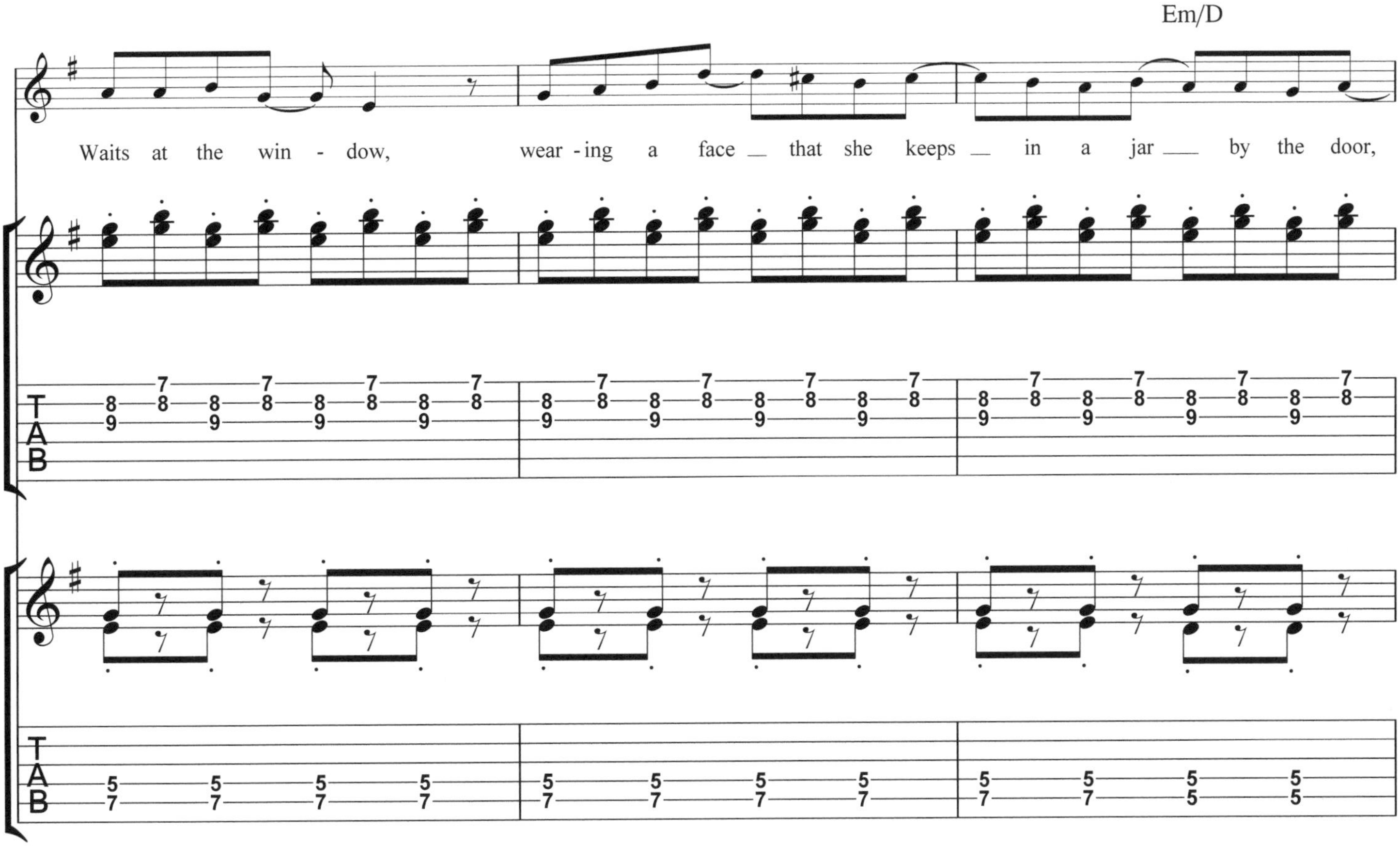
Em/D
Waits at the win - dow, wear - ing a face that she keeps in a jar by the door,

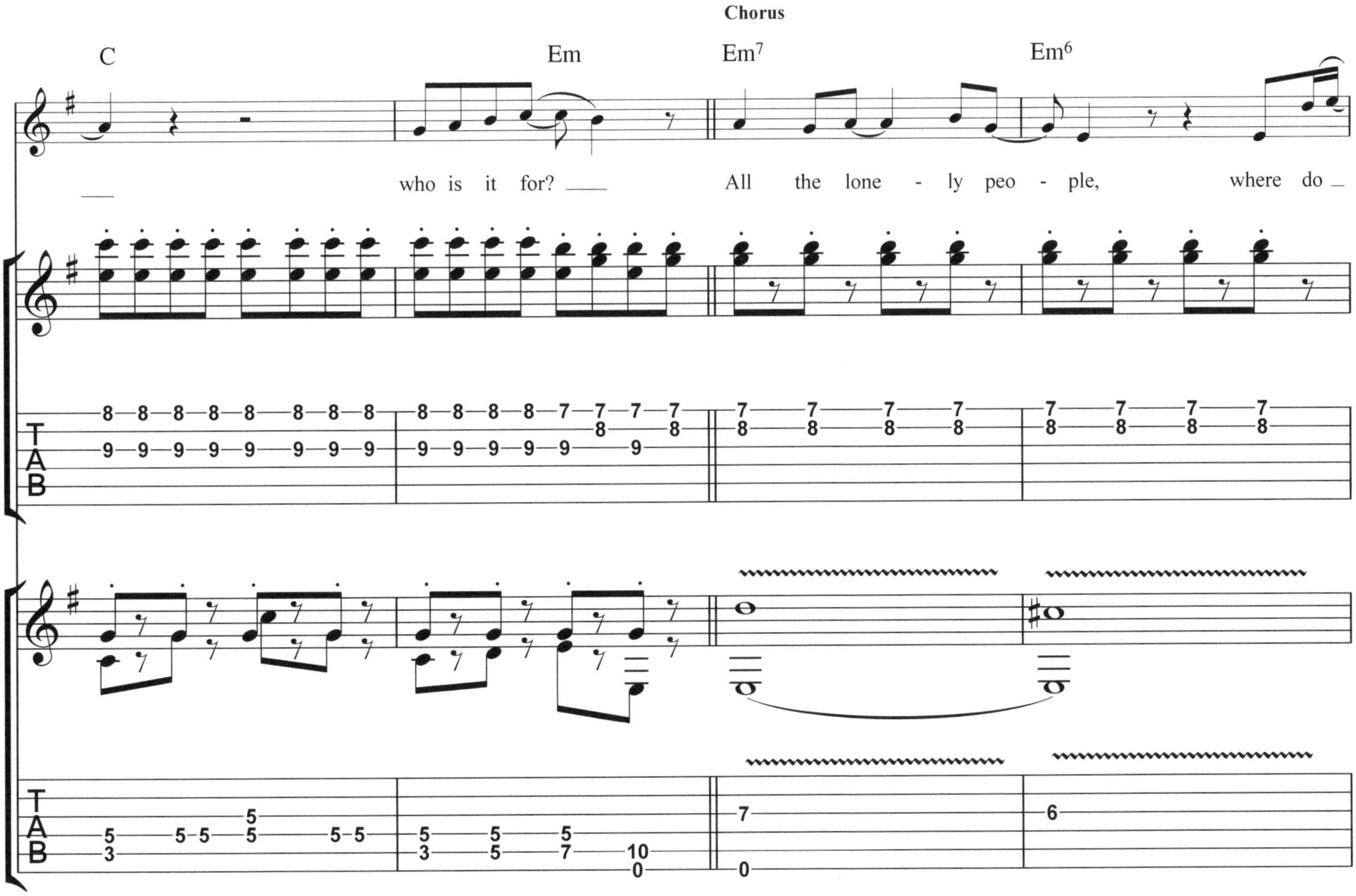
Chorus
C Em Em7 Em6
who is it for? All the lone - ly peo - ple, where do

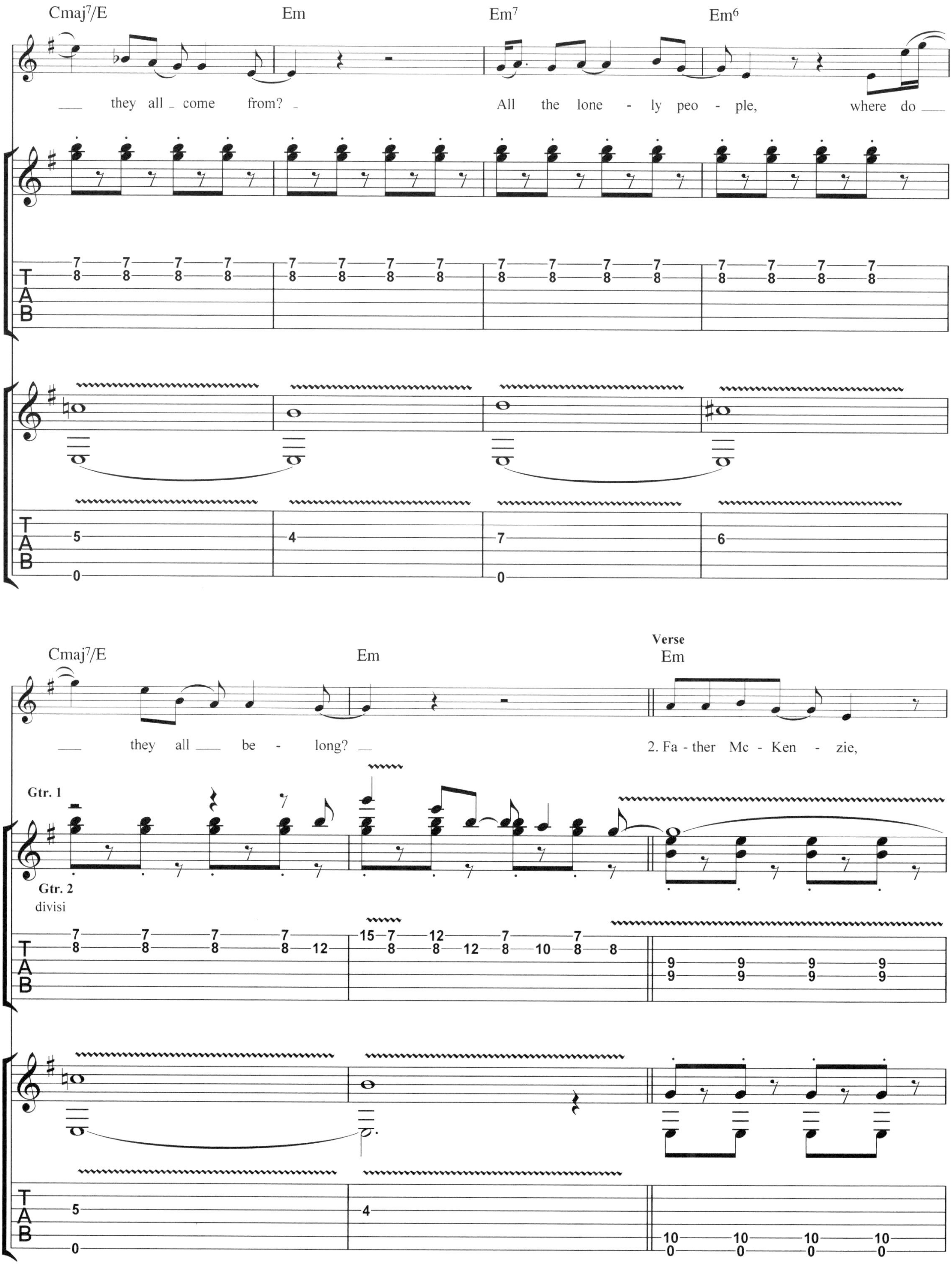
Cmaj7/E
Em
Em7
Em6
they all come from?
All the lone - ly peo - ple, where do
Cmaj7/E
Em
Verse
Em
they all be - long?
2. Fa - ther Mc - Ken - zie,
Gtr. 1
Gtr. 2
divisi

C
writ - ing the words of a ser - mon that no ___ one will hear, ___ no ___
P.T. on
Em
___ one comes near. _ Look at him work - ing, darn - ing his socks in the night _
(P.T. off)

C
Em
when there's no - bod - y there.
What does he care?
P.T. on
(P.T. off)
Chorus
Em7
Em6
Cmaj7/E
Em
All the lone - ly peo - ple, where do they all come from?

Em7
Em6
Cmaj7/E
Em
All the lone - ly peo - ple, where do they all be - long?
C
Em
Ah, look at all the lone - ly peo - ple.

C
Ah, look at all the lone - ly peo -
P.T. on
(P.T. off)
Em
- ple.
Verse
Em
3. El - ea - nor Rig - by

C
died in the church and was bur - ied a - long with her name,
Em
no - bod - y came.
Fa - ther Mc - Ken - zie, wip - ing the dirt from his hands
TAB

C6
Em
as he walks from the grave,
no one was saved.
Chorus
Em7
Em6
Cmaj7/E
Ah, look at all the lone - ly peo - ple.
All the lone - ly peo - ple, where do they all come from?

Em
Em7
Em6
Ah, look at all the lone - ly peo -
All the lone - ly peo - ple, where do
Cmaj7/E
Em
- ple.
they all be - long?

PENNY LANE

Words & Music by John Lennon & Paul McCartney

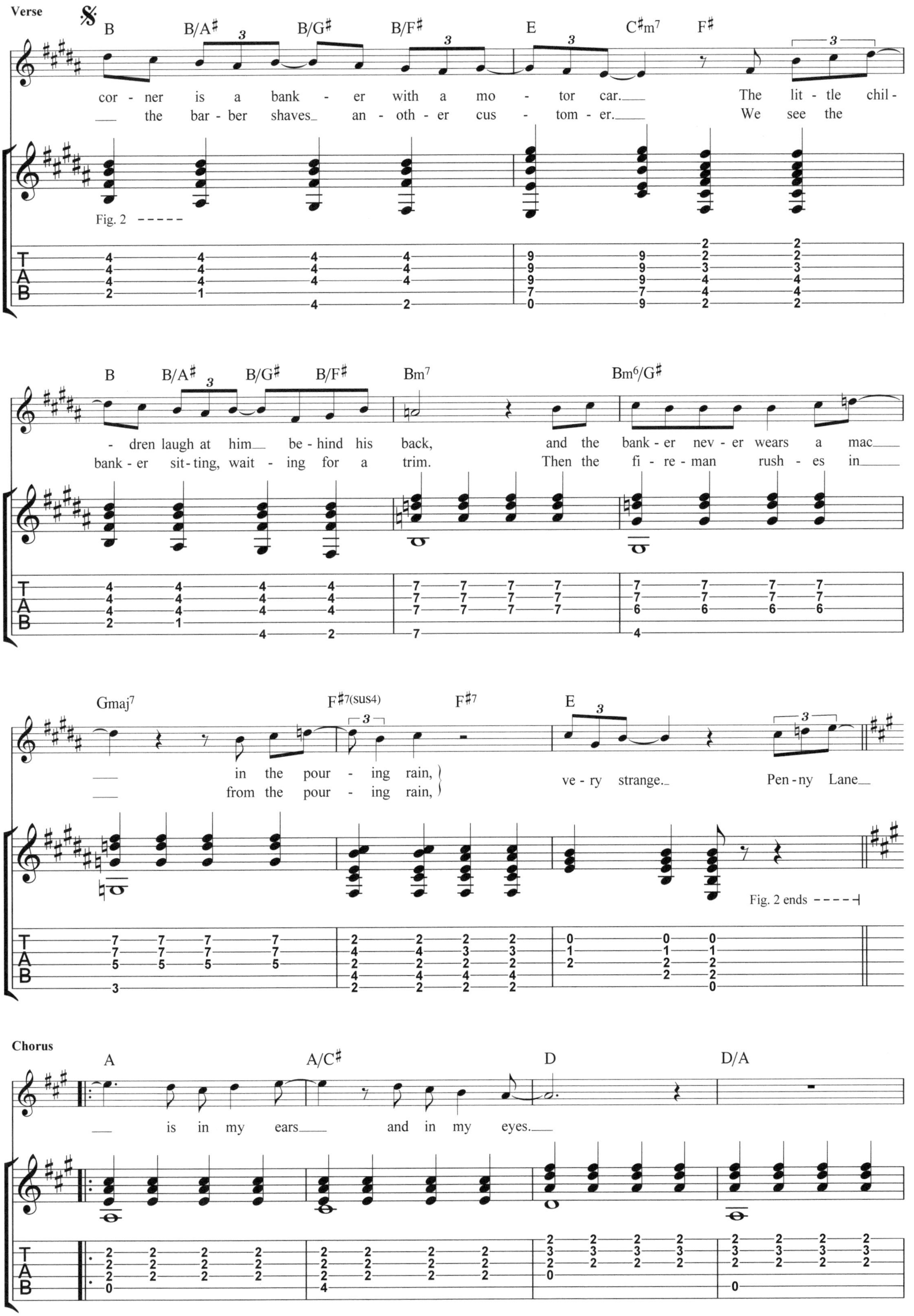
Verse
B B/A♯ B/G♯ B/F♯ E C♯m7 F♯
corner is a banker with a motor car. The little chil-
the barber shaves another customer. We see the
Fig. 2
B B/A♯ B/G♯ B/F♯ Bm7 Bm6/G♯
-dren laugh at him behind his back, and the banker never wears a mac
banker sitting, waiting for a trim. Then the fireman rushes in
Gmaj7 F♯7(sus4) F♯7 E
in the pouring rain,
from the pouring rain,
very strange. Penny Lane
Fig. 2 ends
Chorus
A A/C♯ D D/A
is in my ears and in my eyes.

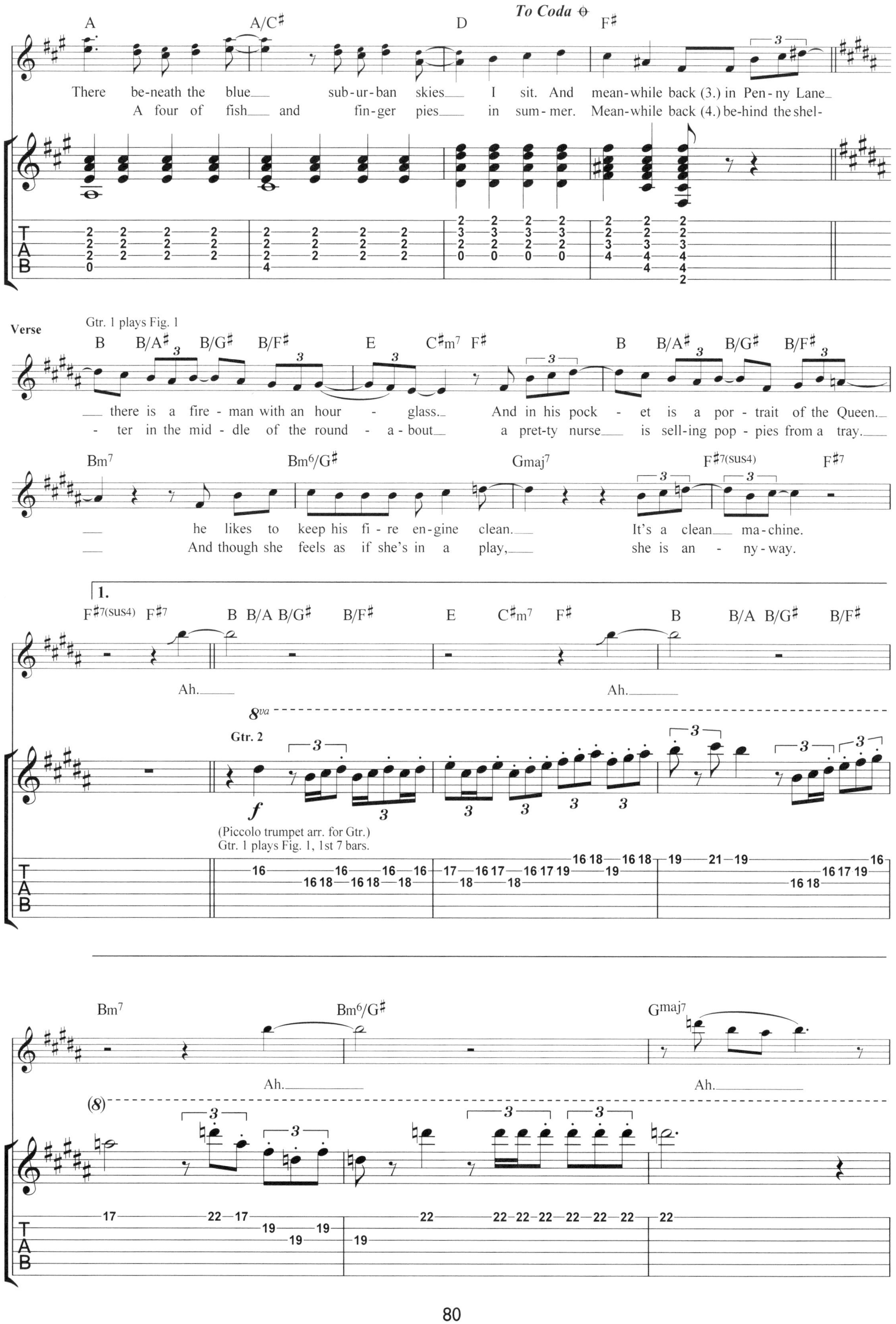
To Coda
A A/C♯ D F♯
There be-neath the blue sub-ur-ban skies I sit. And mean-while back (3.) in Pen-ny Lane
A four of fish and fin-ger pies in sum-mer. Mean-while back (4.) be-hind the shel-
Verse
Gtr. 1 plays Fig. 1
B B/A♯ B/G♯ B/F♯ E C♯m7 F♯ B B/A♯ B/G♯ B/F♯
there is a fire-man with an hour-glass. And in his pock-et is a por-trait of the Queen.
-ter in the mid-dle of the round-a-bout a pret-ty nurse is sell-ing pop-pies from a tray.
Bm7 Bm6/G♯ Gmaj7 F♯7(sus4) F♯7
he likes to keep his fi-re en-gine clean. It's a clean ma-chine.
And though she feels as if she's in a play, she is an-ny-way.
1.
F♯7(sus4) F♯7 B B/A B/G♯ B/F♯ E C♯m7 F♯ B B/A B/G♯ B/F♯
Ah. Ah.
8va
Gtr. 2
f
(Piccolo trumpet arr. for Gtr.)
Gtr. 1 plays Fig. 1, 1st 7 bars.
Bm7 Bm6/G♯ Gmaj7
Ah. Ah.
(8)

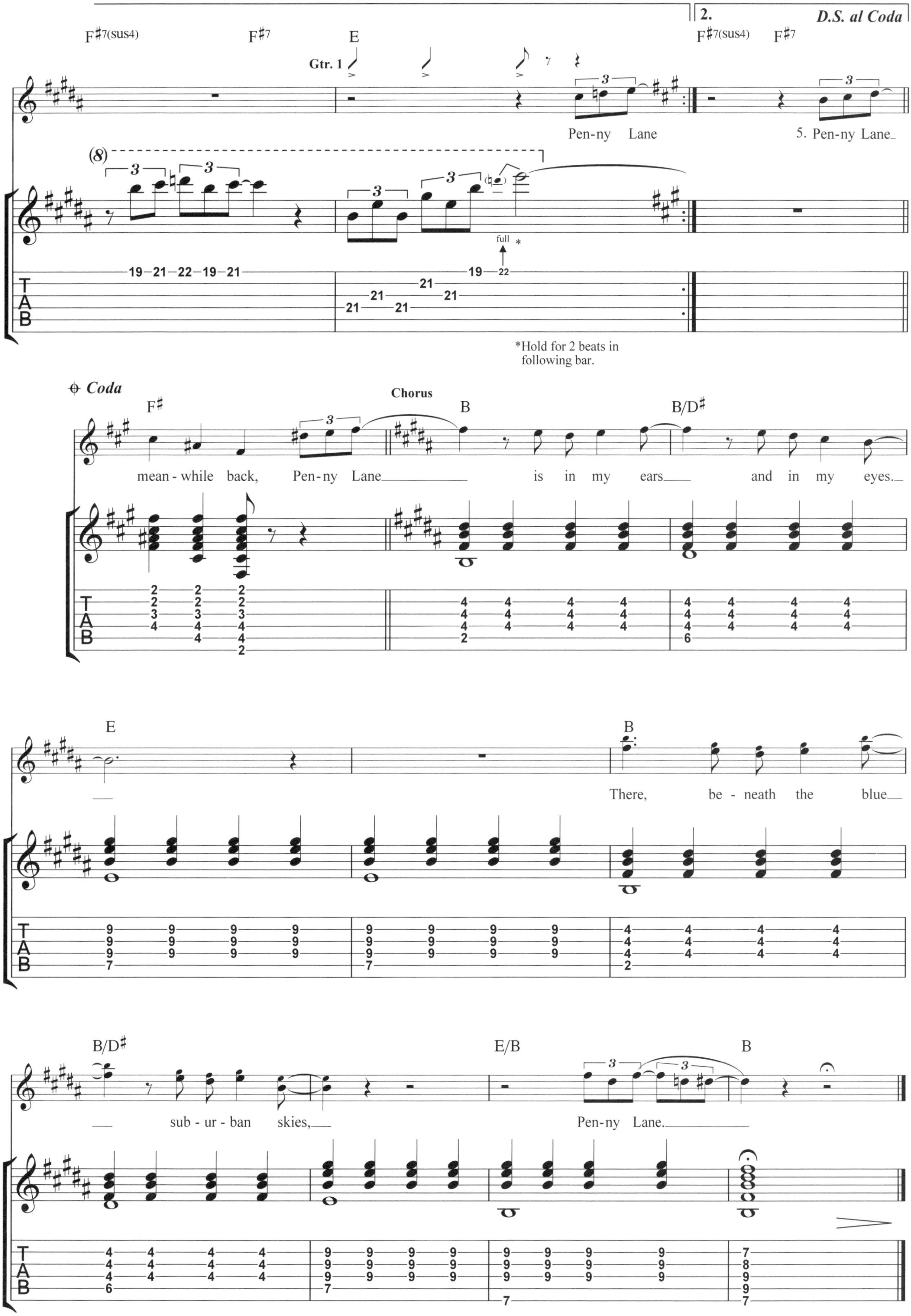
2.
D.S. al Coda
F♯7(sus4)
F♯7
E
Gtr. 1
Pen-ny Lane
5. Pen-ny Lane
(8)
full
*Hold for 2 beats in following bar.
Coda
F♯
Chorus
B
B/D♯
mean-while back, Pen-ny Lane is in my ears and in my eyes.
E
B
There, be-neath the blue
B/D♯
E/B
B
sub-ur-ban skies, Pen-ny Lane.

HELLO, GOODBYE

Words & Music by John Lennon & Paul McCartney

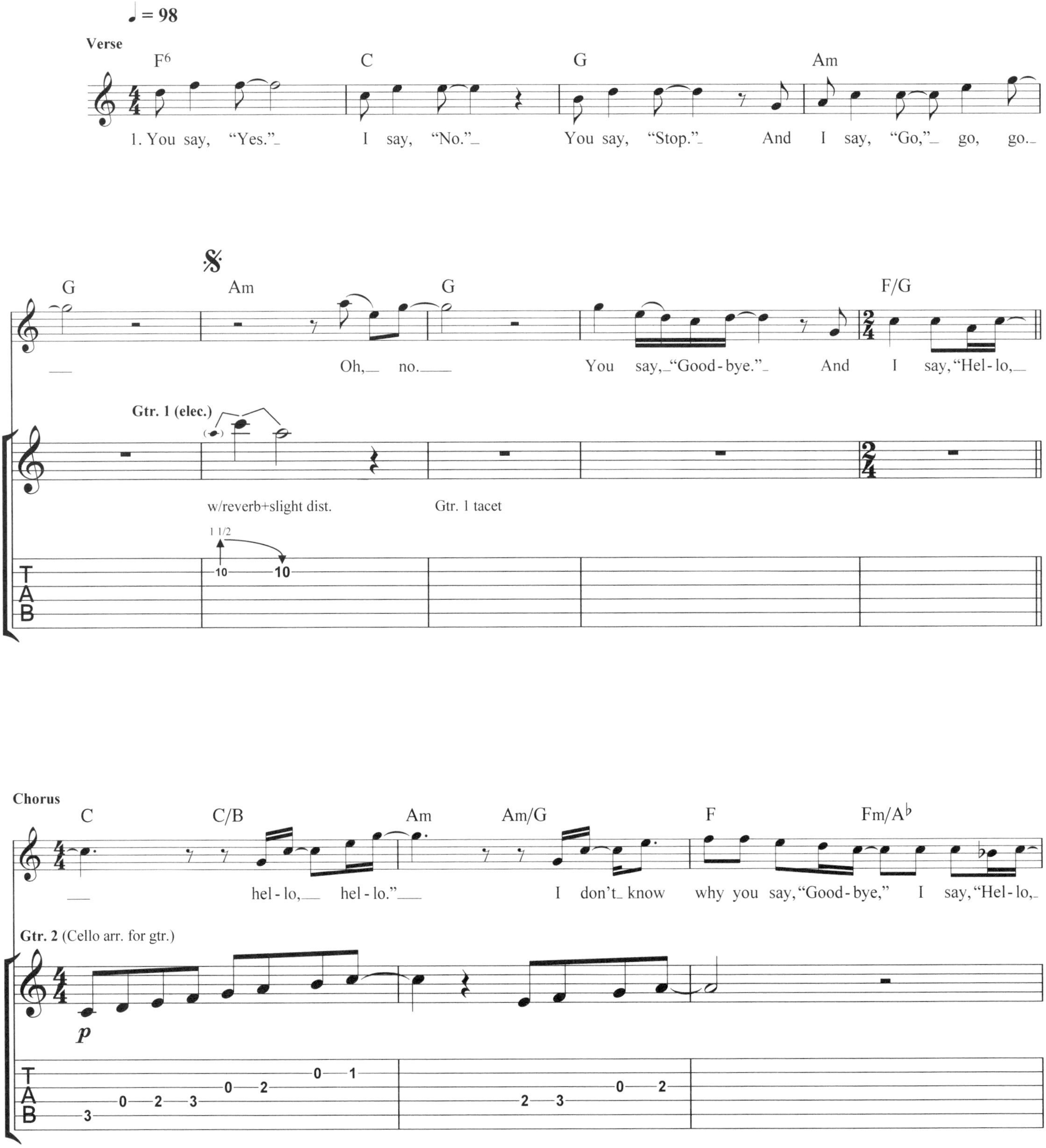

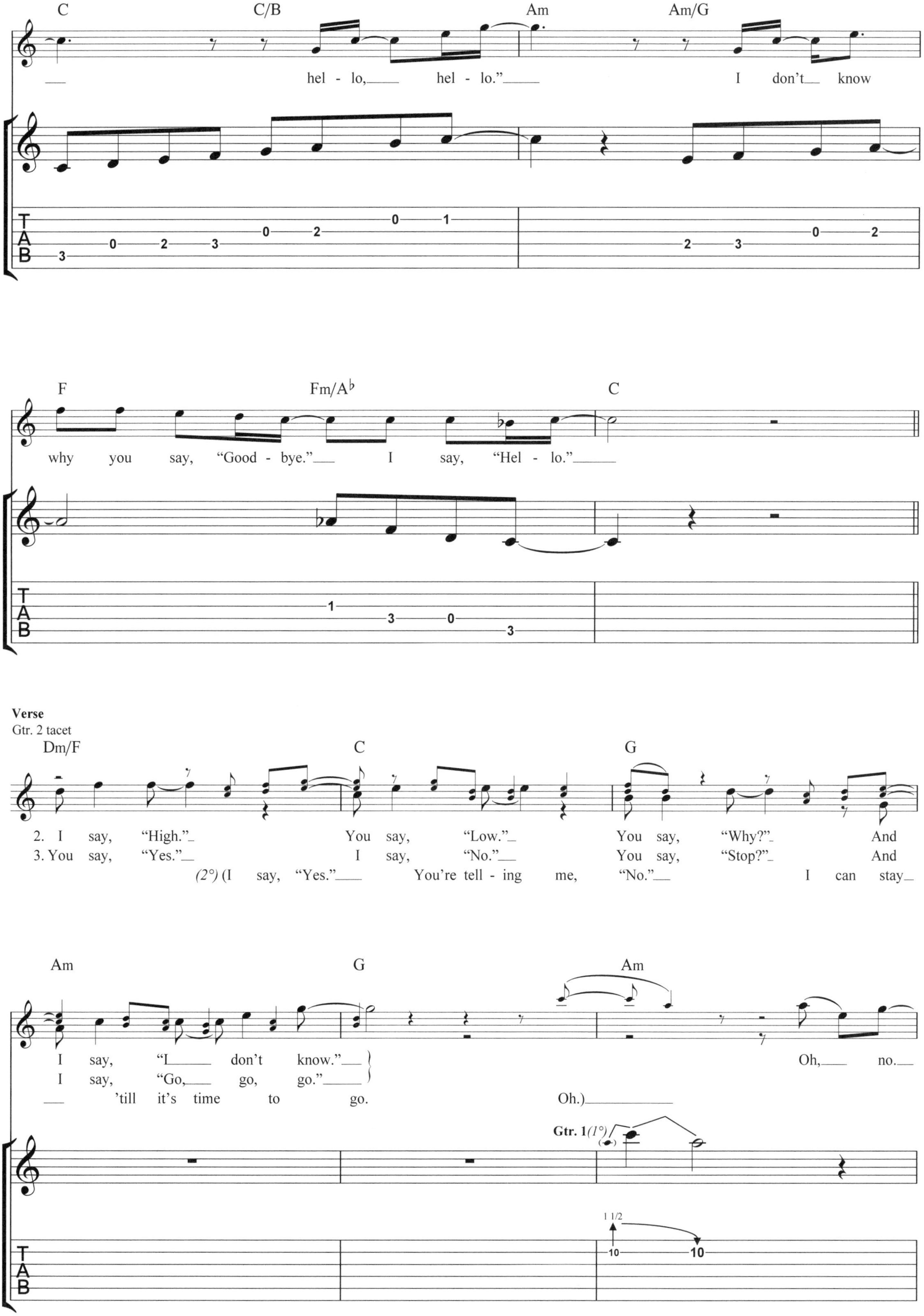
C
C/B
Am
Am/G
hel - lo, hel - lo." I don't know
F
Fm/A♭
C
why you say, "Good - bye." I say, "Hel - lo."
Verse
Gtr. 2 tacet
Dm/F
C
G
2. I say, "High." You say, "Low." You say, "Why?" And
3. You say, "Yes." I say, "No." You say, "Stop?" And
(2°) (I say, "Yes." You're tell - ing me, "No." I can stay
Am
G
Am
I say, "I don't know." Oh, no.
I say, "Go, go, go."
'till it's time to go. Oh.)
Gtr. 1 (1°)
1 1/2
T
A
B

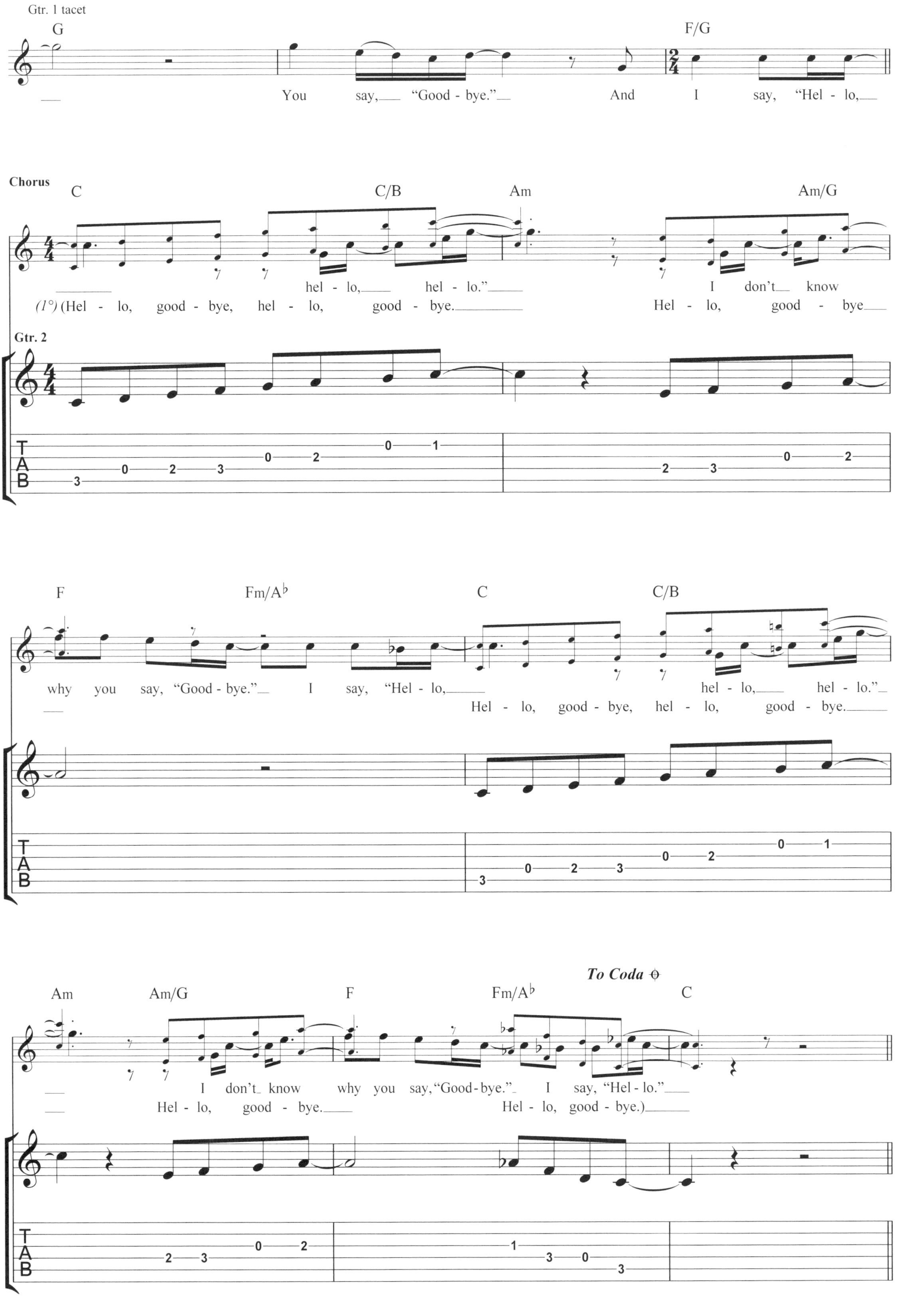
Gtr. 1 tacet
G
F/G
You say, "Good - bye." And I say, "Hel - lo,
Chorus
C C/B Am Am/G
hel - lo, hel - lo." I don't know
(1°) (Hel - lo, good - bye, hel - lo, good - bye. Hel - lo, good - bye
Gtr. 2
F Fm/A♭ C C/B
why you say, "Good - bye." I say, "Hel - lo, hel - lo, hel - lo."
Hel - lo, good - bye, hel - lo, good - bye.
Am Am/G F Fm/A♭
To Coda
C
I don't know why you say, "Good-bye." I say, "Hel - lo."
Hel - lo, good - bye. Hel - lo, good - bye.)

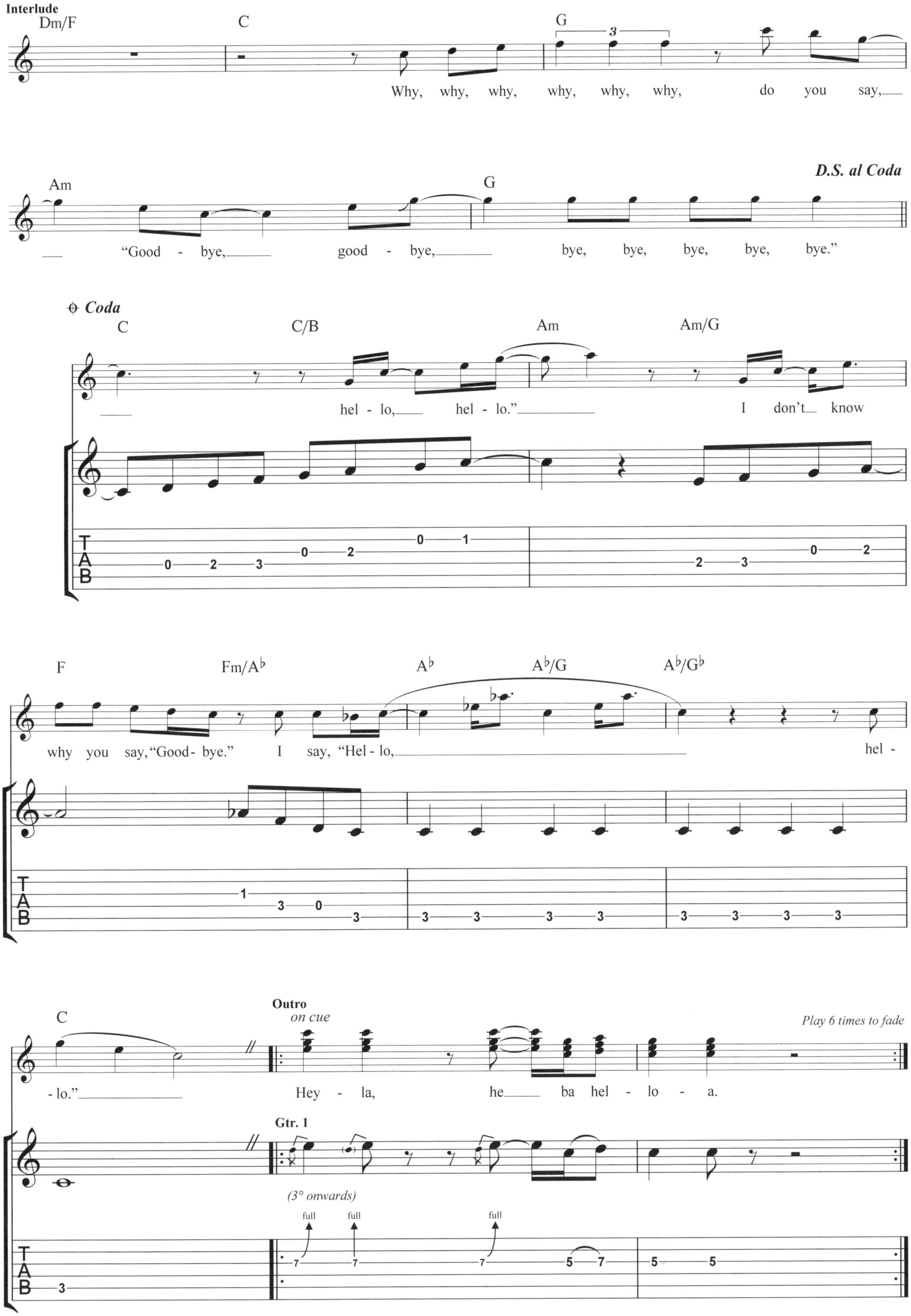
Interlude
Dm/F C G
Why, why, why, why, why, why, do you say,
Am G
D.S. al Coda
"Good - bye, good - bye, bye, bye, bye, bye, bye."
Coda
C C/B Am Am/G
hel - lo, hel - lo." I don't know
F Fm/A♭ A♭ A♭/G A♭/G♭
why you say, "Good - bye." I say, "Hel - lo, hel -
C
Outro
on cue
Play 6 times to fade
- lo." Hey - la, he ba hel - lo - a.
Gtr. 1
(3° onwards)
full
full
full

ALL YOU NEED IS LOVE

Words & Music by John Lennon & Paul McCartney

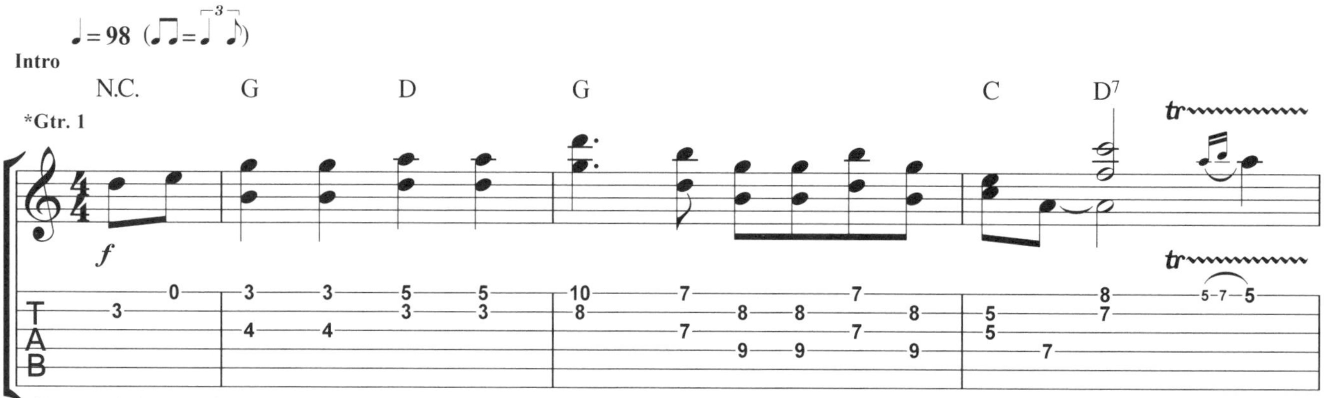

*Brass and piano arr. for gtr.

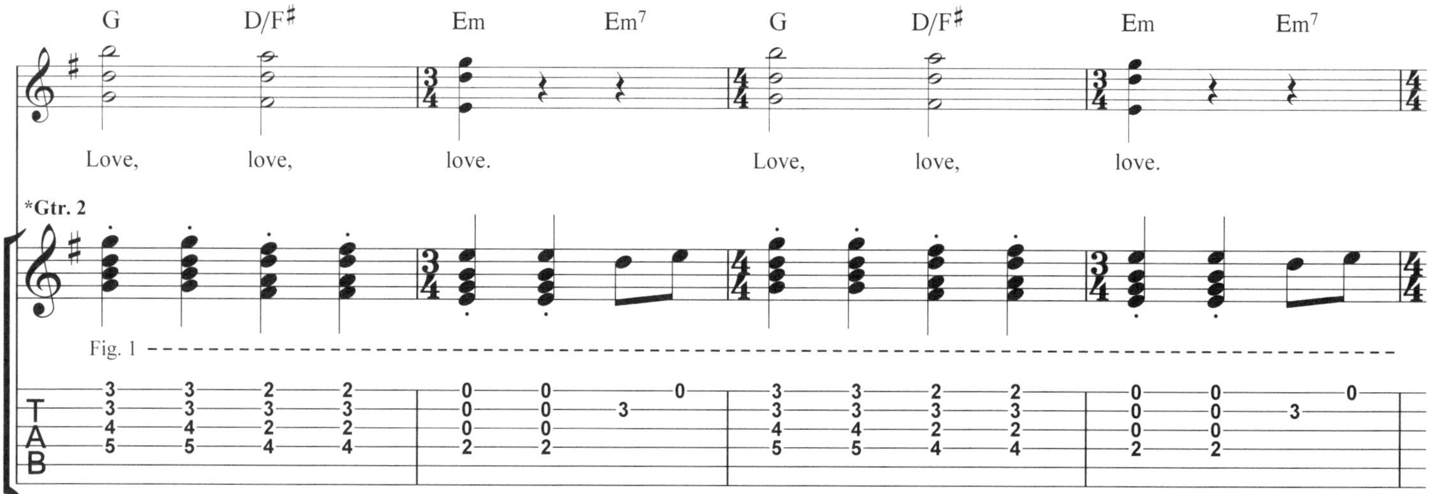

*Harpsichord arr. for gtr.

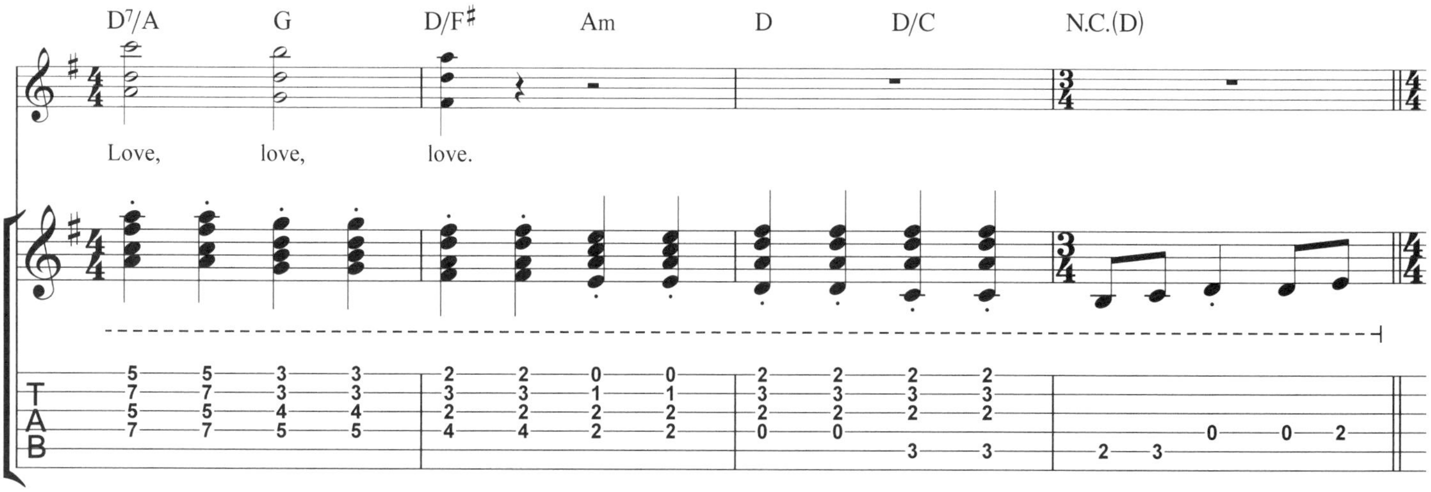

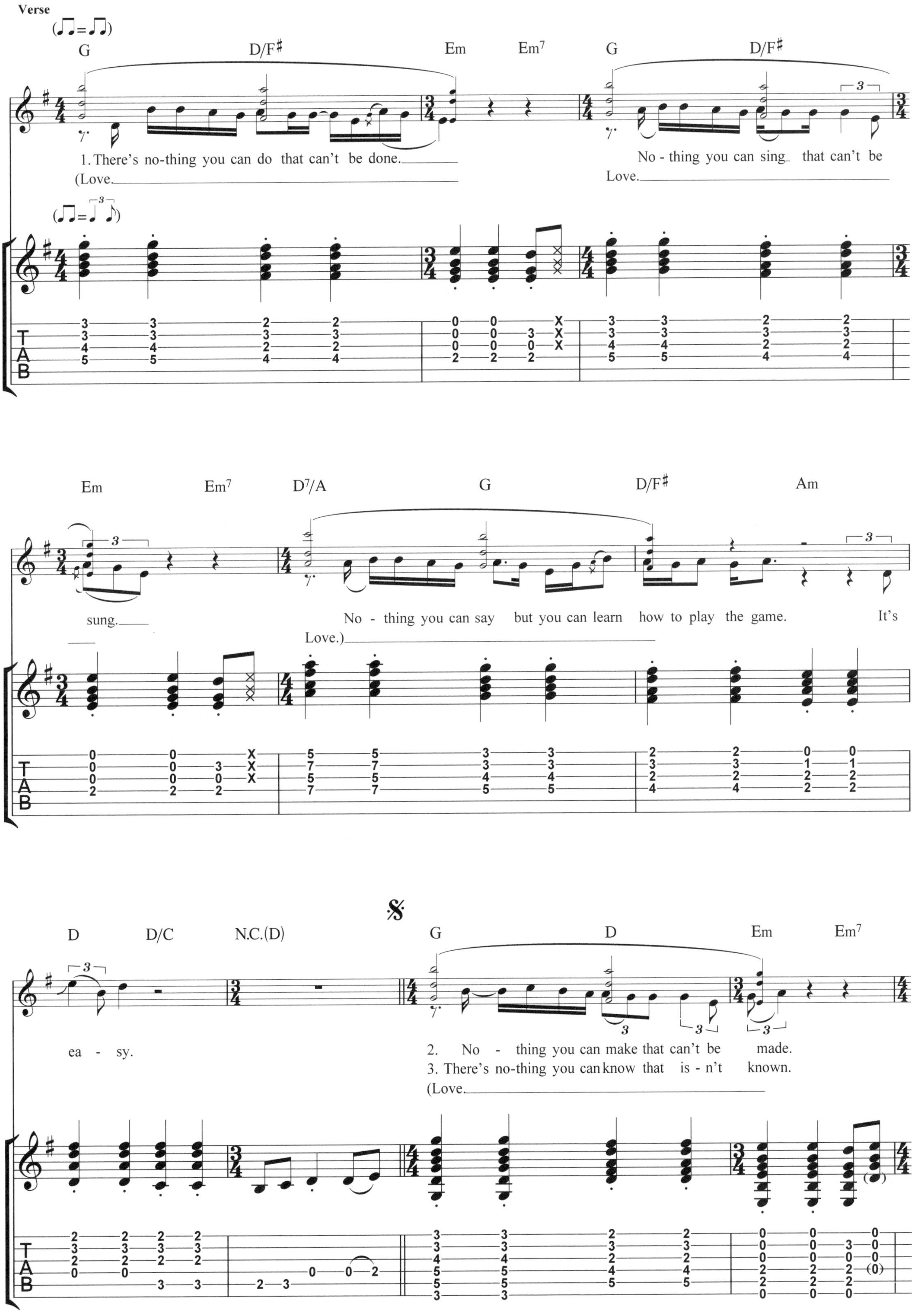
Verse
G D/F♯ Em Em7 G D/F♯
1. There's no-thing you can do that can't be done.
(Love.
No - thing you can sing that can't be
Love.
Em Em7 D7/A G D/F♯ Am
sung.
No - thing you can say but you can learn how to play the game. It's
Love.)
D D/C N.C.(D) G D Em Em7
ea - sy.
2. No - thing you can make that can't be made.
3. There's no-thing you can know that is - n't known.
(Love.

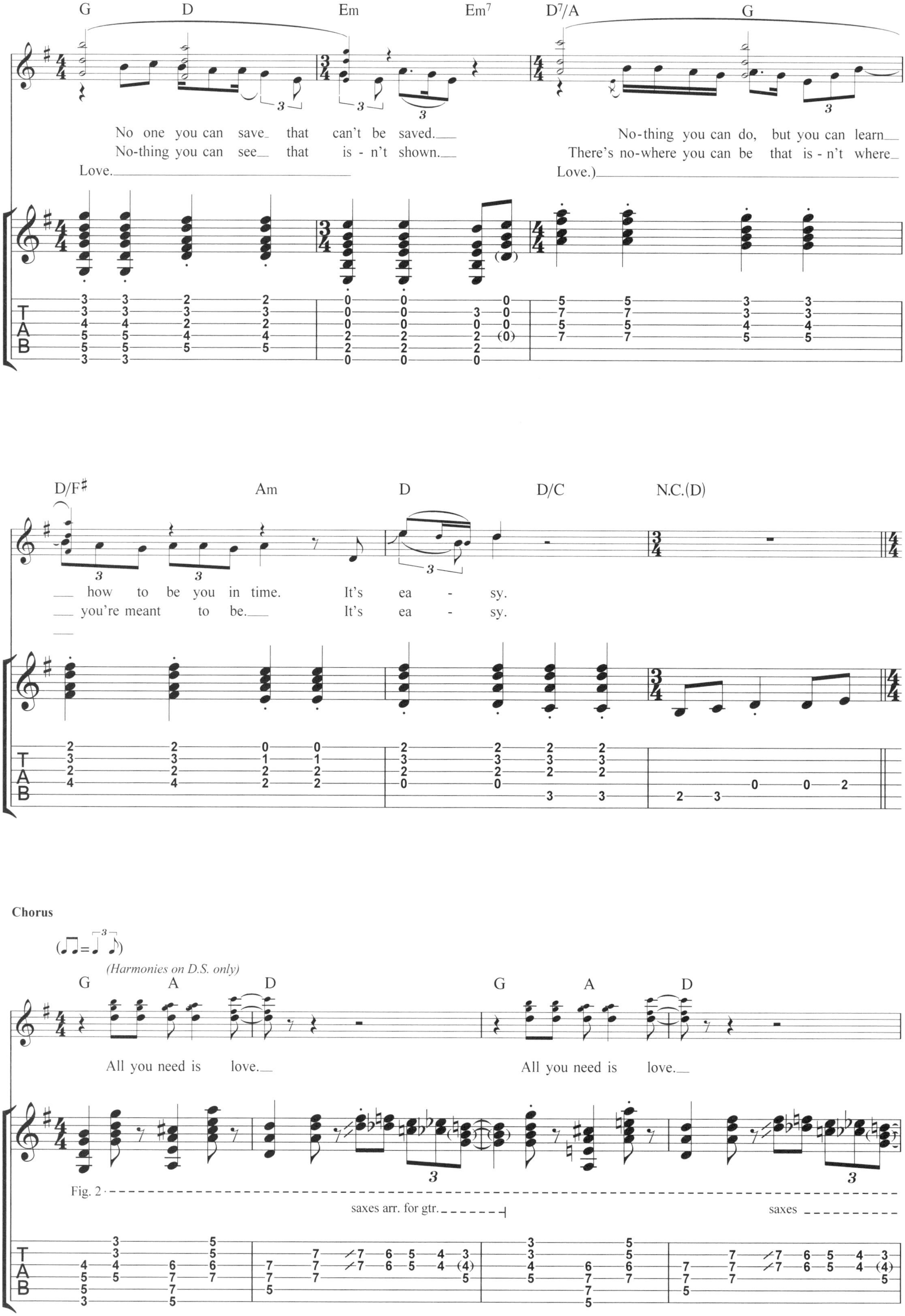
G D Em Em7 D7/A G
No one you can save that can't be saved.
No-thing you can see that is-n't shown.
Love.
No-thing you can do, but you can learn
There's no-where you can be that is-n't where
Love.)
D/F♯ Am D D/C N.C.(D)
how to be you in time. It's ea - sy.
you're meant to be. It's ea - sy.
Chorus
(Harmonies on D.S. only)
G A D G A D
All you need is love. All you need is love.
Fig. 2
saxes arr. for gtr.
saxes

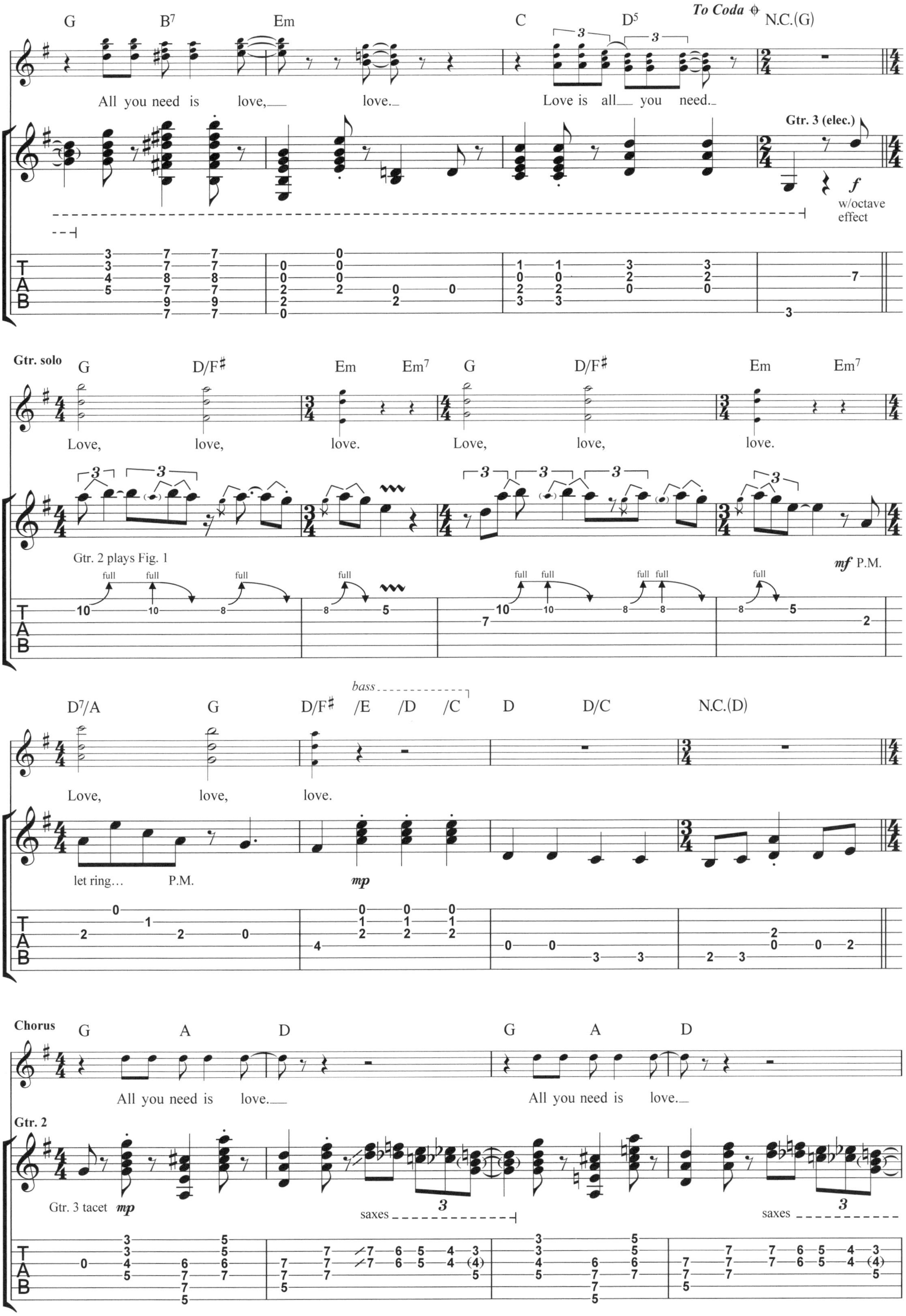

G B7 Em C D5
To Coda
N.C.(G)
All you need is love, love. Love is all you need.
Gtr. 3 (elec.)
w/octave effect
Gtr. solo
G D/F♯ Em Em7 G D/F♯ Em Em7
Love, love, love. Love, love, love.
Gtr. 2 plays Fig. 1
full
mf P.M.
D7/A G D/F♯ /E /D /C D D/C N.C.(D)
bass
Love, love, love.
let ring…
P.M.
mp
Chorus
G A D G A D
All you need is love. All you need is love.
Gtr. 2
Gtr. 3 tacet
mp
saxes

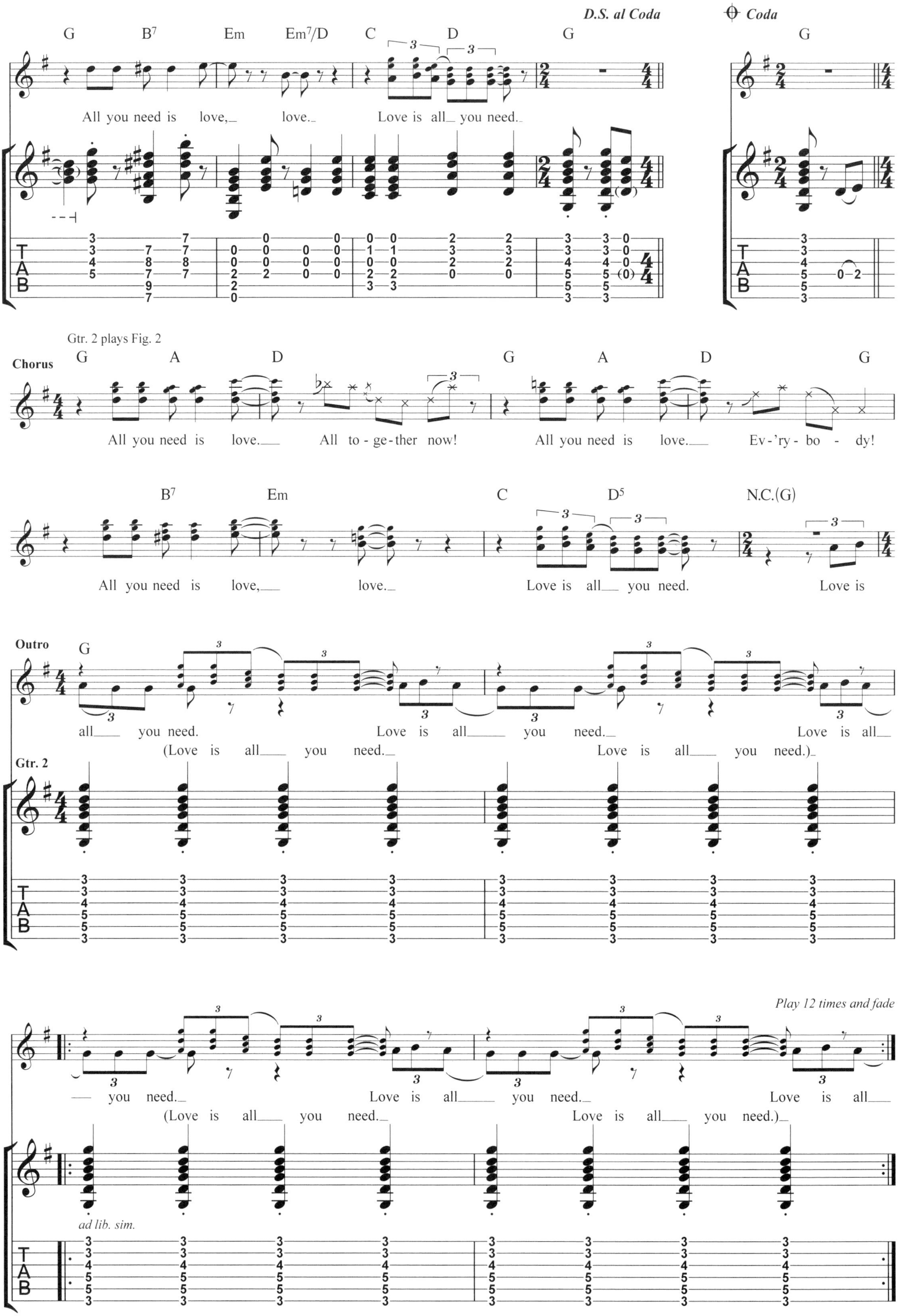
D.S. al Coda
Coda
G B7 Em Em7/D C D G
All you need is love, love. Love is all you need.
G
Gtr. 2 plays Fig. 2
Chorus
G A D G A D G
All you need is love. All to-ge-ther now! All you need is love. Ev-'ry-bo-dy!
B7 Em C D5 N.C.(G)
All you need is love, love. Love is all you need. Love is
Outro
G
all you need. Love is all you need. Love is all
(Love is all you need. Love is all you need.)
Gtr. 2
you need. Love is all you need. Love is all
(Love is all you need. Love is all you need.)
ad lib. sim.
Play 12 times and fade

SOMETHING

Words & Music by George Harrison

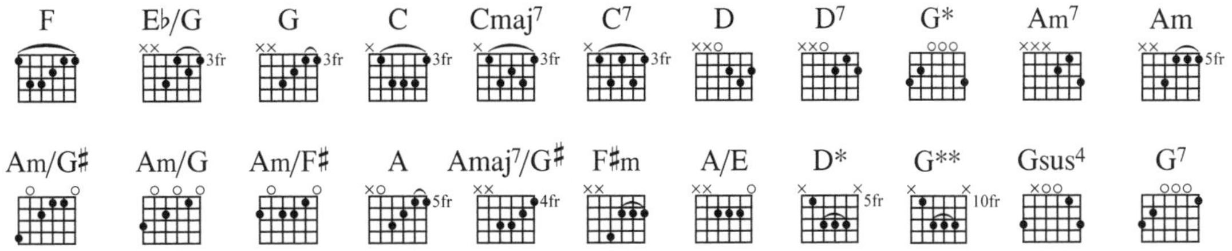

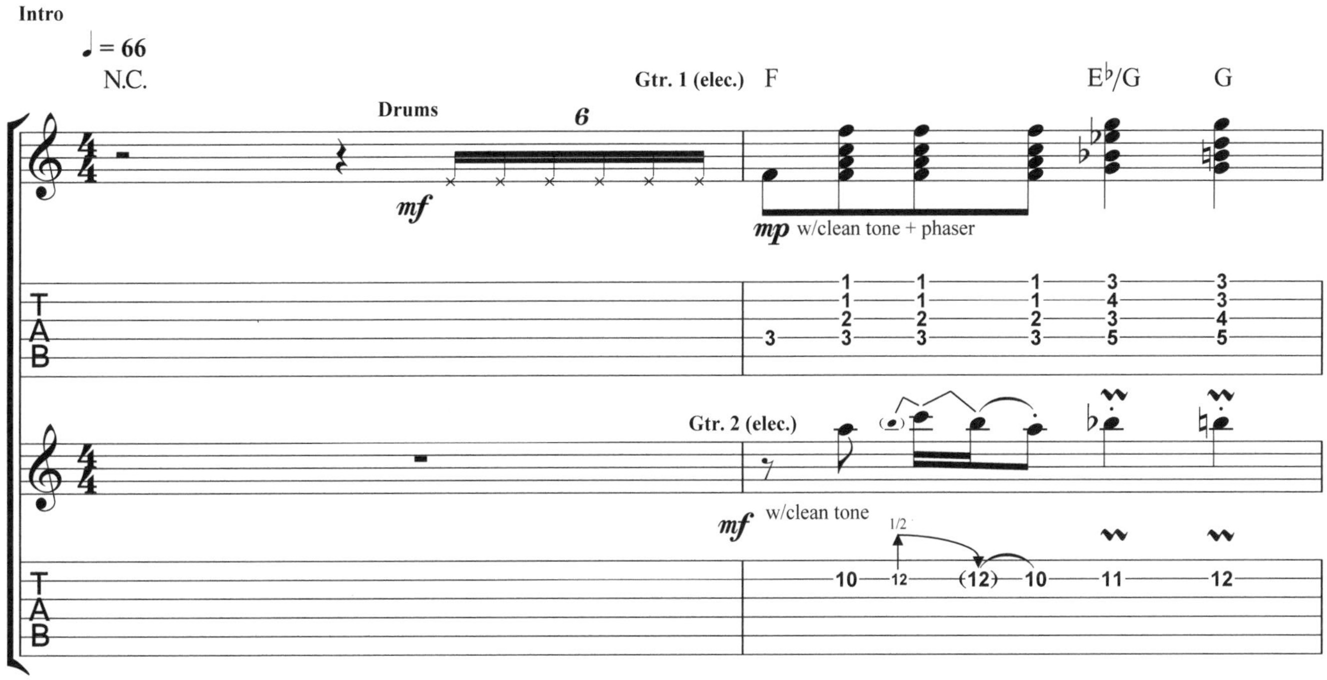

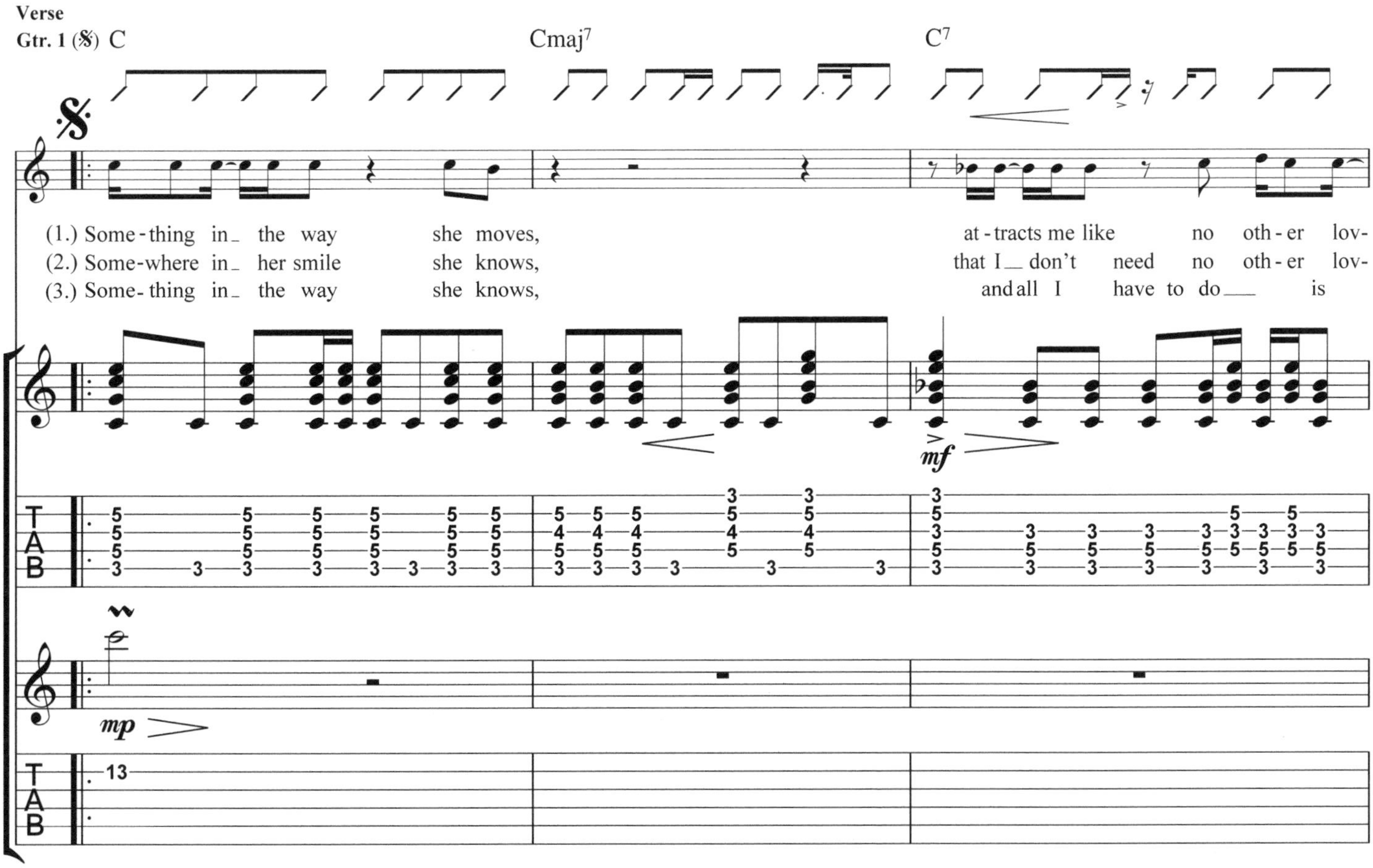

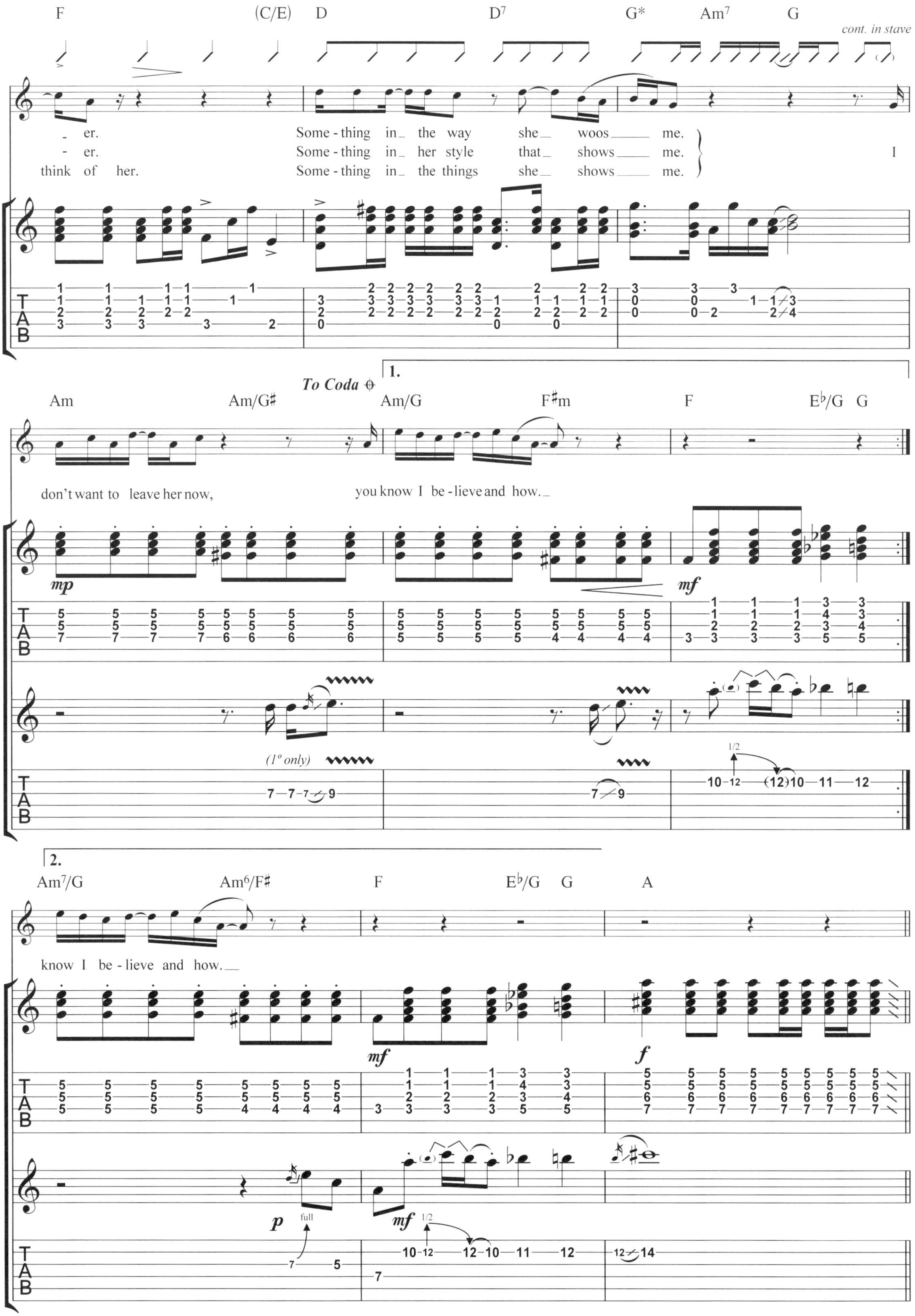
F (C/E) D D7 G* Am7 G
cont. in stave
- er. Some - thing in the way she woos me.
- er. Some - thing in her style that shows me. I
think of her. Some - thing in the things she shows me.
To Coda
1.
Am Am/G♯ Am/G F♯m F E♭/G G
don't want to leave her now, you know I be - lieve and how.
mp
mf
(1º only)
1/2
2.
Am7/G Am6/F♯ F E♭/G G A
know I be - lieve and how.
mf
f
p
full
1/2

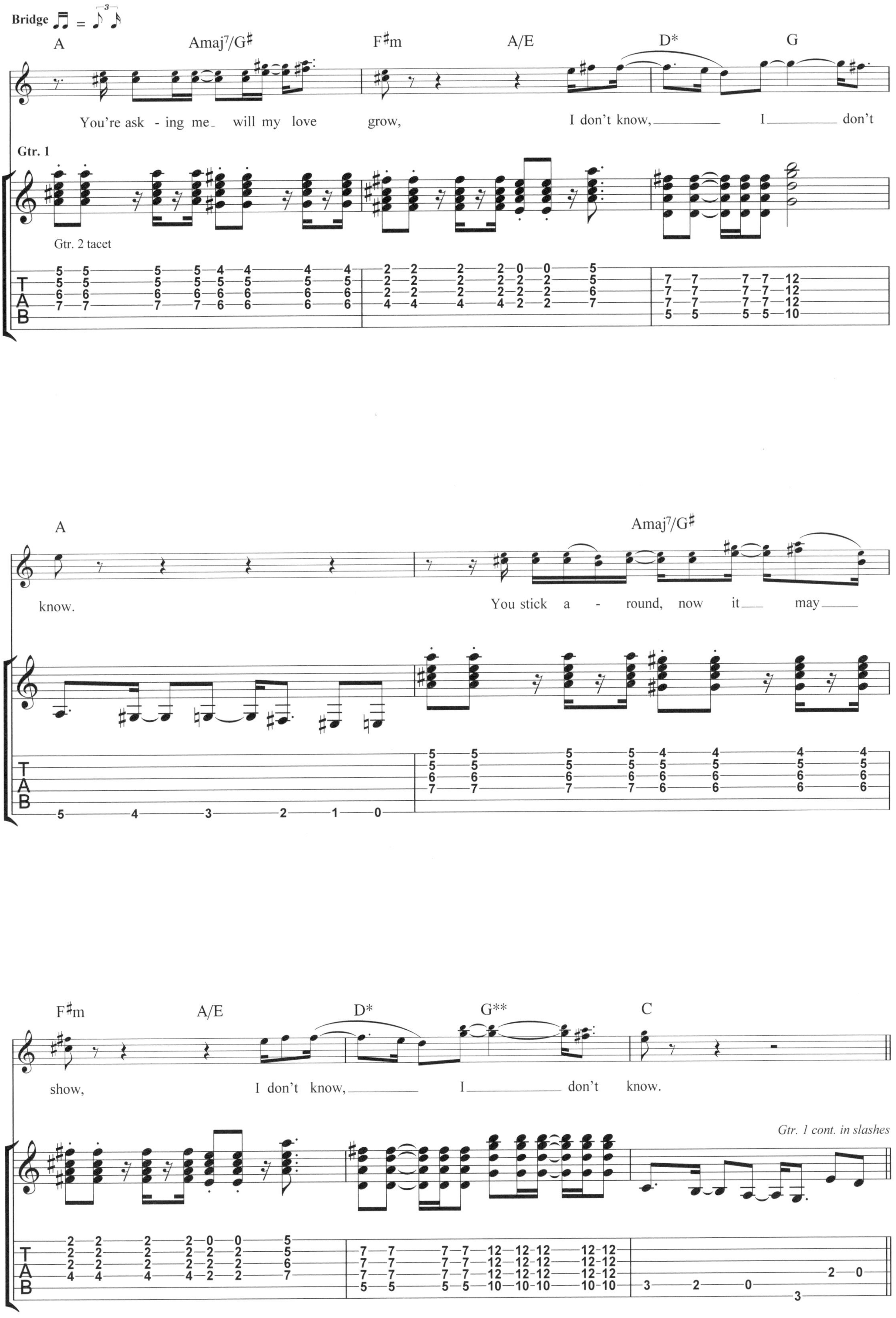
Bridge
A Amaj7/G# F#m A/E D* G
You're ask - ing me will my love grow, I don't know, I don't
Gtr. 1
Gtr. 2 tacet
A Amaj7/G#
know. You stick a - round, now it may
F#m A/E D* G** C
show, I don't know, I don't know.
Gtr. 1 cont. in slashes

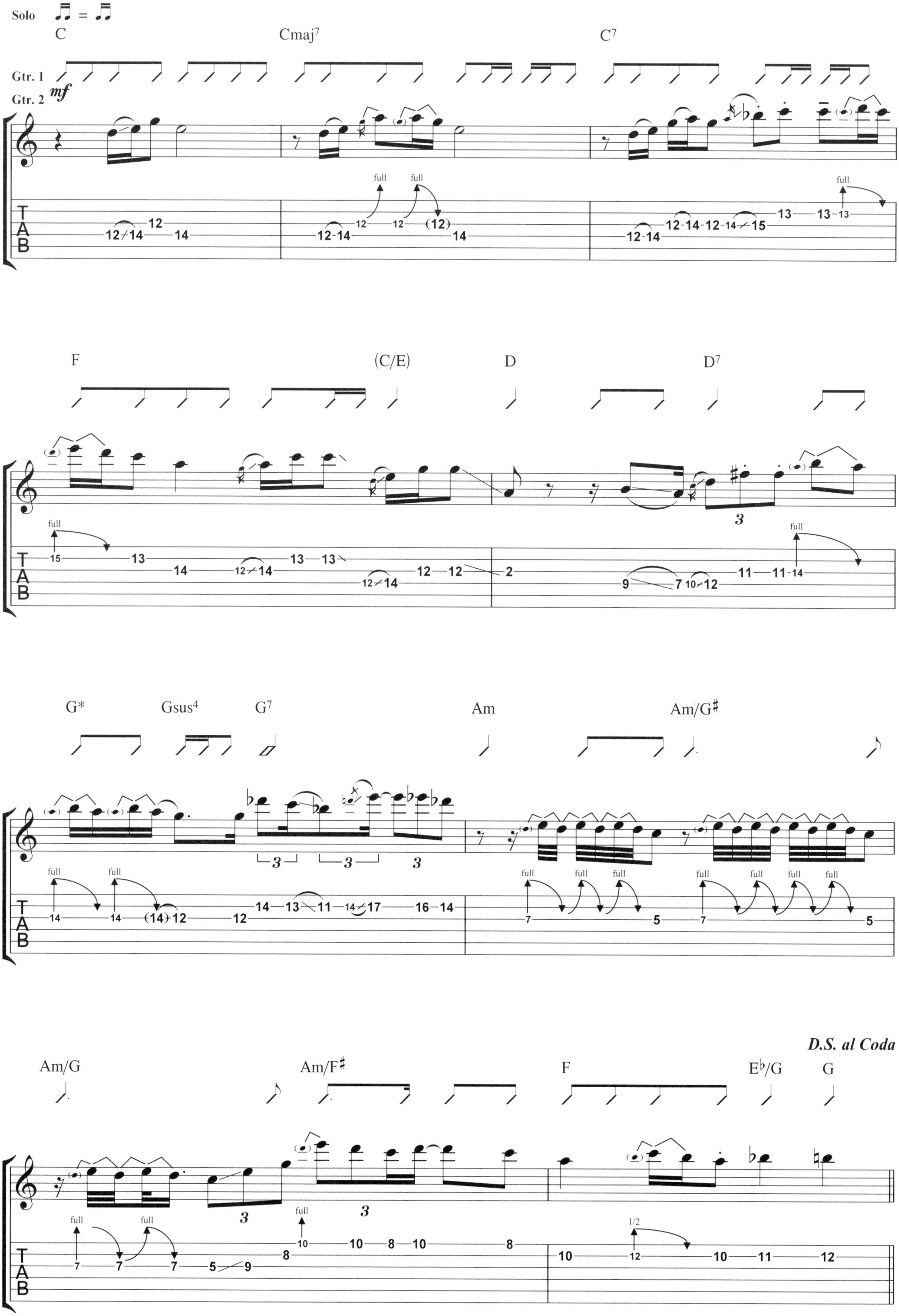

Solo
C
Cmaj7
C7
Gtr. 1
Gtr. 2
mf
full
F
(C/E)
D
D7
G*
Gsus4
G7
Am
Am/G♯
D.S. al Coda
Am/G
Am/F♯
E♭/G
G
1/2

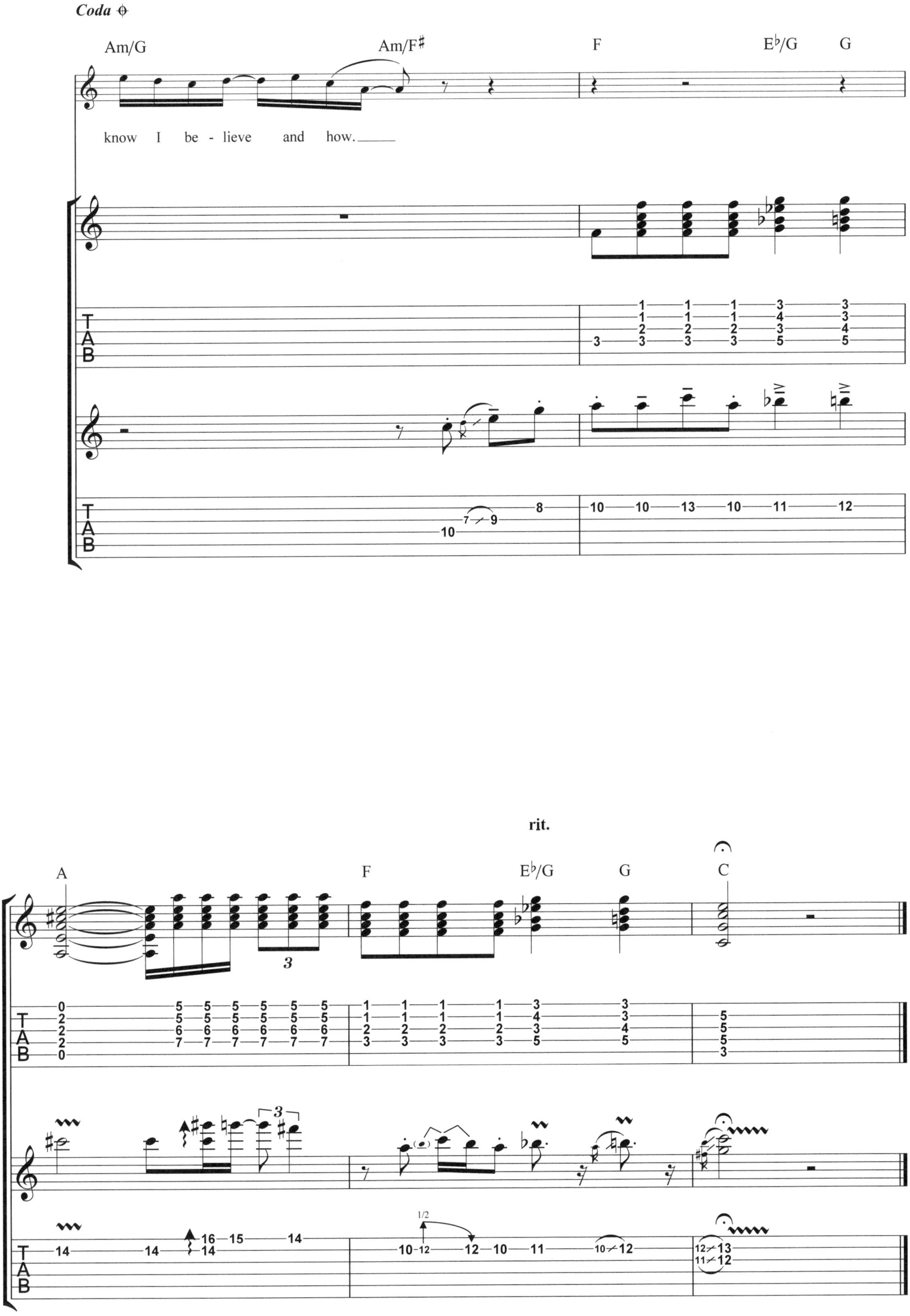
Coda
Am/G
Am/F♯
F
E♭/G
G
know I be - lieve and how.
rit.
A
F
E♭/G
G
C
1/2

LADY MADONNA

Words & Music by John Lennon & Paul McCartney

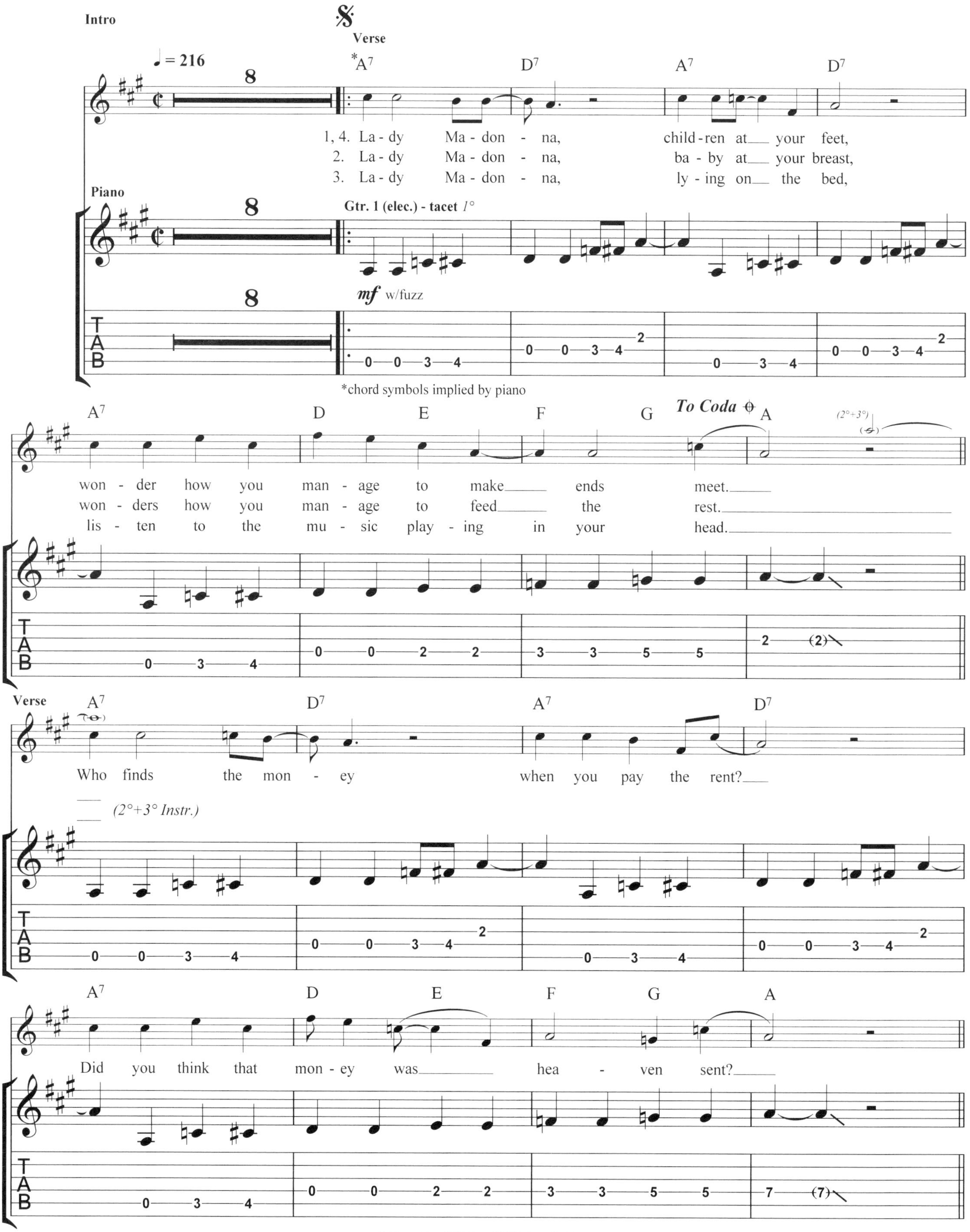

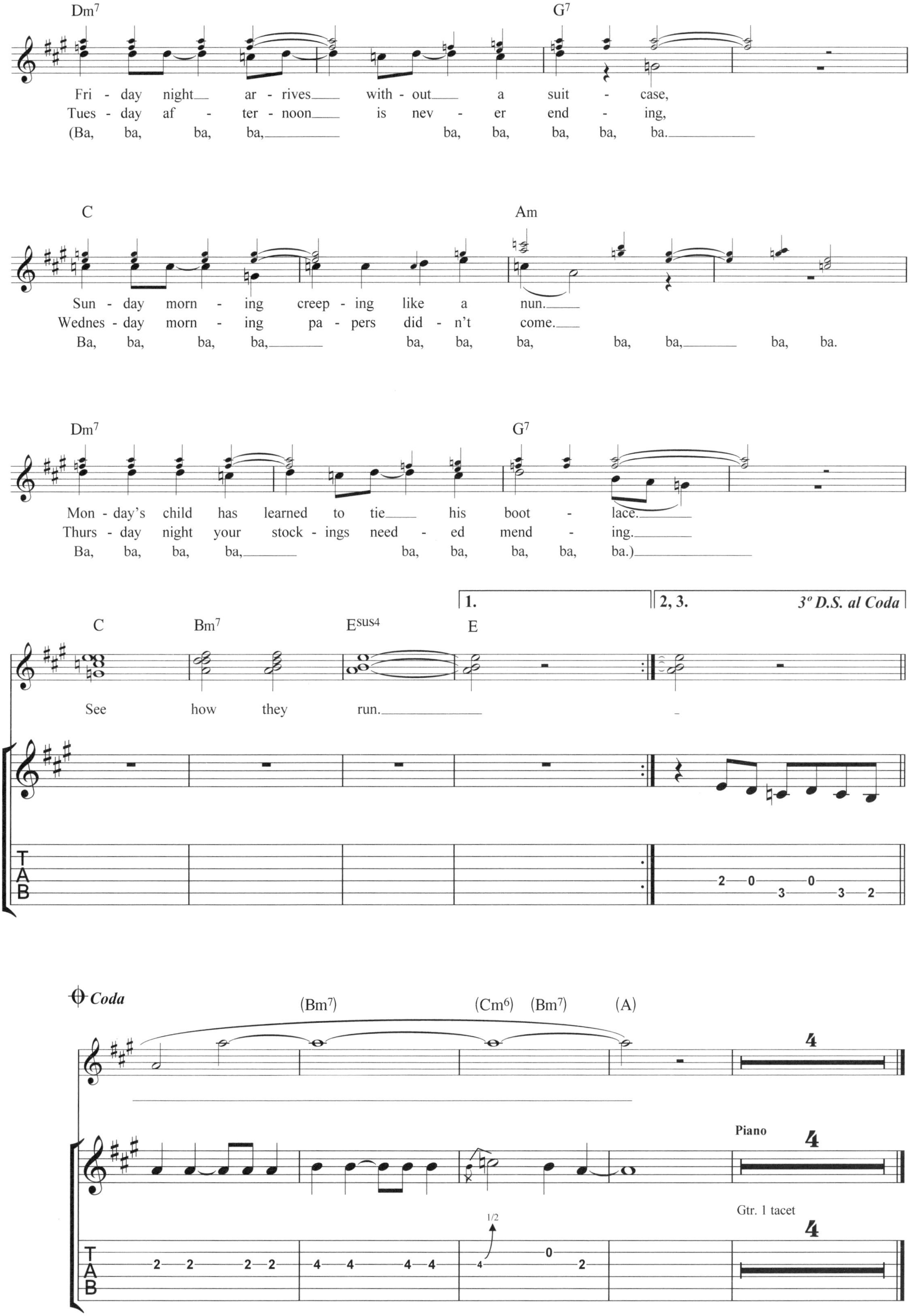
Dm7
G7
Fri - day night ar - rives with - out a suit - case,
Tues - day af - ter - noon is nev - er end - ing,
(Ba, ba, ba, ba, ba, ba, ba, ba, ba.
C
Am
Sun - day morn - ing creep - ing like a nun.
Wednes - day morn - ing pa - pers did - n't come.
Ba, ba, ba, ba, ba, ba, ba, ba, ba, ba, ba.
Dm7
G7
Mon - day's child has learned to tie his boot - lace.
Thurs - day night your stock - ings need - ed mend - ing.
Ba, ba, ba, ba, ba, ba, ba, ba, ba.)
1.
2, 3.
3º D.S. al Coda
C
Bm7
Esus4
E
See how they run.
Coda
(Bm7)
(Cm6)
(Bm7)
(A)
Piano
Gtr. 1 tacet
4

HEY JUDE

Words & Music by John Lennon & Paul McCartney

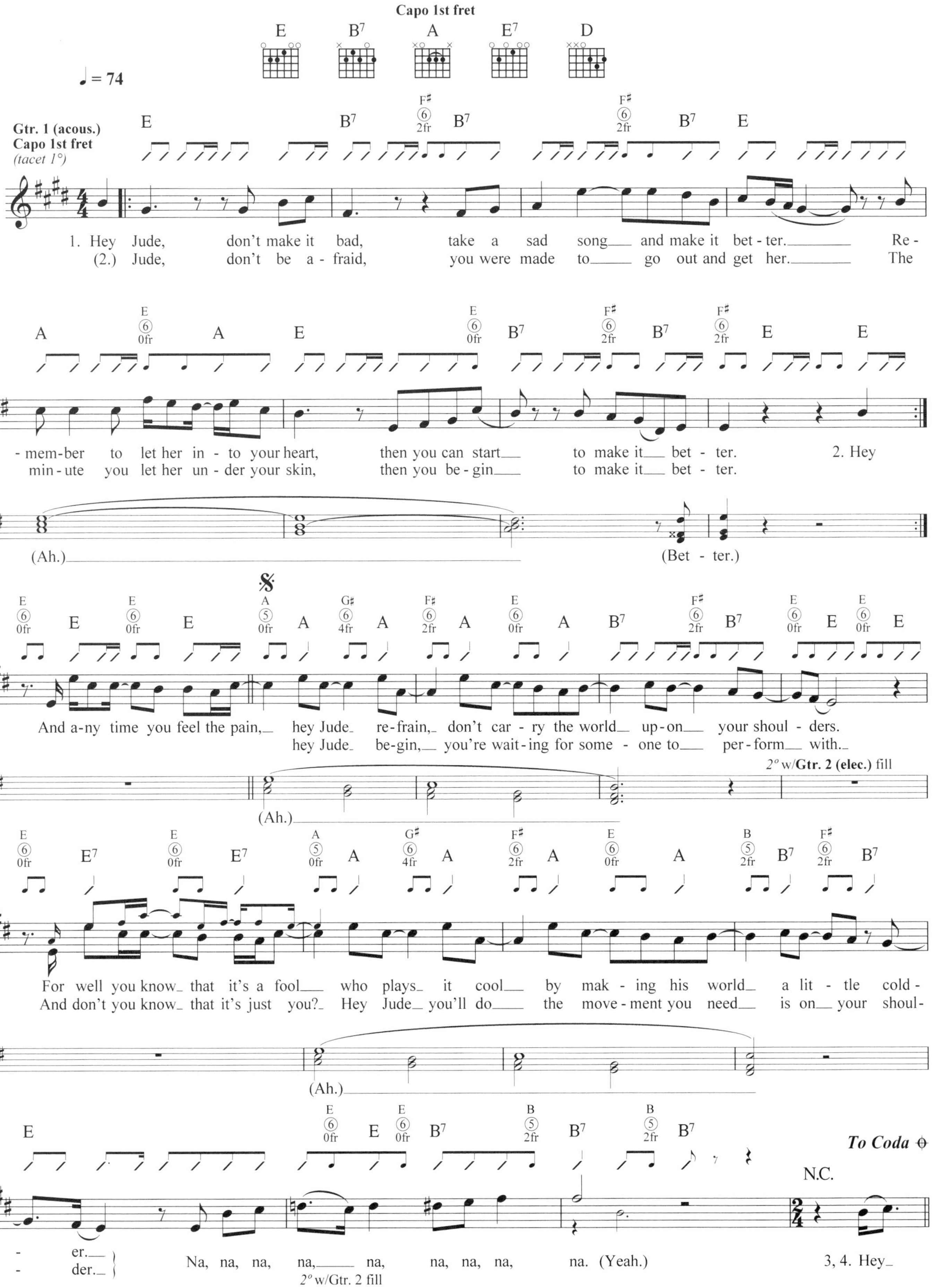

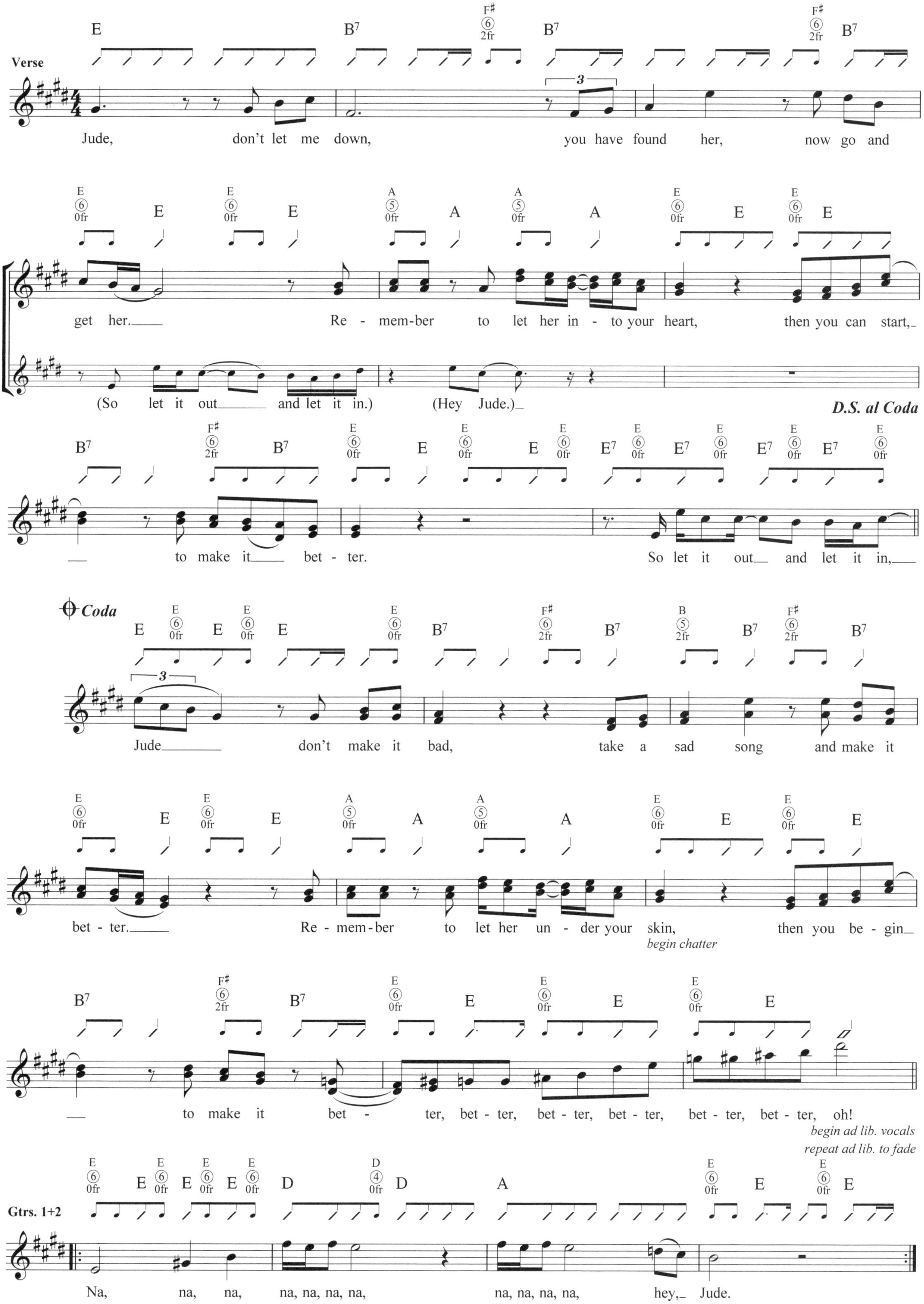
Verse
E B7 F♯ B7 F♯ B7
Jude, don't let me down, you have found her, now go and
get her. Re - mem - ber to let her in - to your heart, then you can start,
(So let it out and let it in.) (Hey Jude.)
D.S. al Coda
B7 F♯ B7 E E E7 E7 E7 E7
to make it bet - ter. So let it out and let it in,
Coda
E E E B7 F♯ B7 B B7 F♯ B7
Jude don't make it bad, take a sad song and make it
E E A A E E
bet - ter. Re - mem - ber to let her un - der your skin, then you be - gin
begin chatter
B7 F♯ B7 E E E
to make it bet - ter, bet - ter, bet - ter, bet - ter, bet - ter, bet - ter, oh!
begin ad lib. vocals
repeat ad lib. to fade
Gtrs. 1+2
E E E E D D A E E
Na, na, na, na, na, na, na, na, na, na, na, hey, Jude.

GET BACK

Words & Music by John Lennon & Paul McCartney

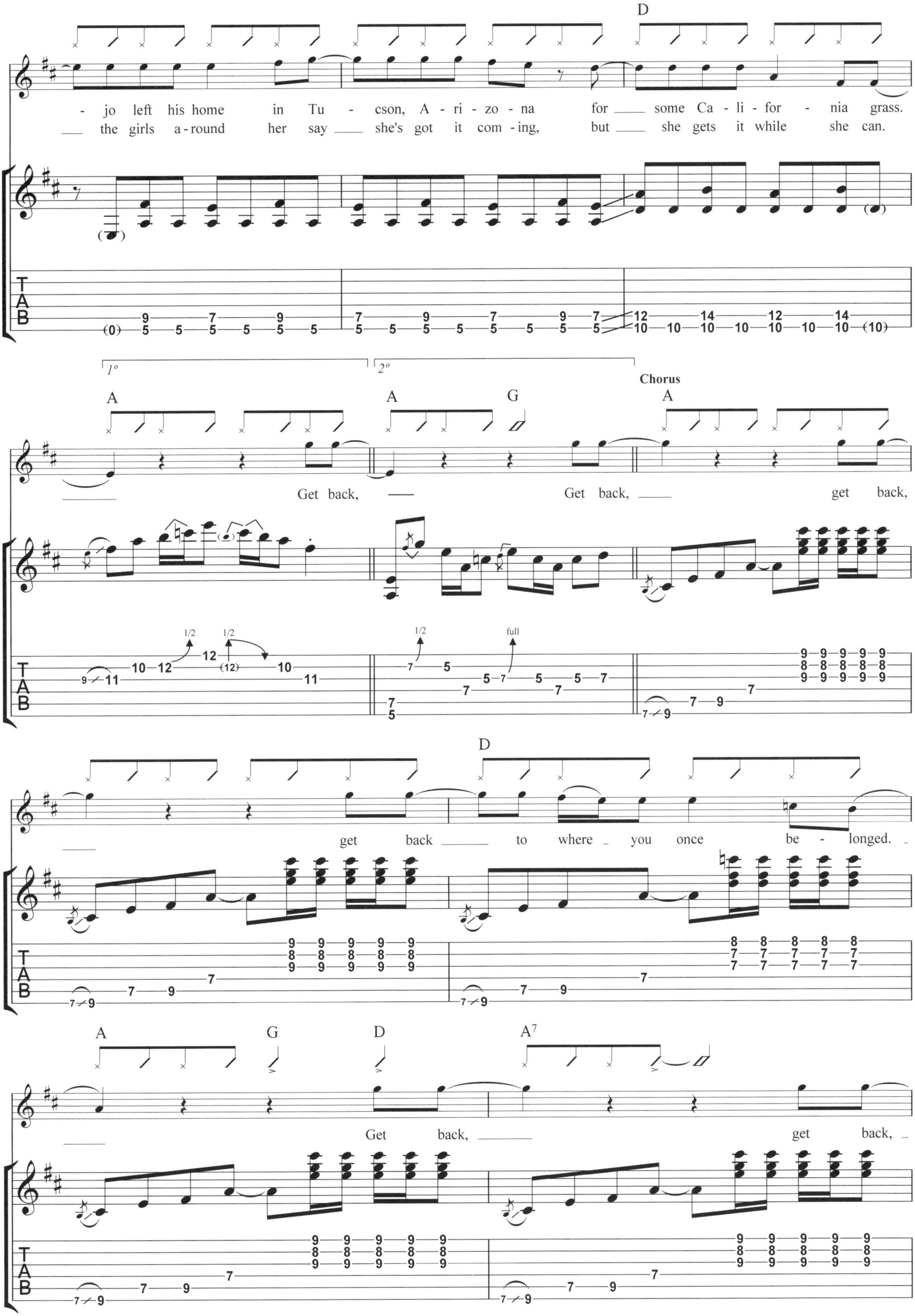
D
-jo left his home in Tu - cson, A - ri - zo - na for some Ca - li - for - nia grass.
the girls a-round her say she's got it com-ing, but she gets it while she can.
1º
2º
Chorus
A
A G
A
Get back, Get back, get back,
D
get back to where you once be - longed.
A G D A7
Get back, get back,

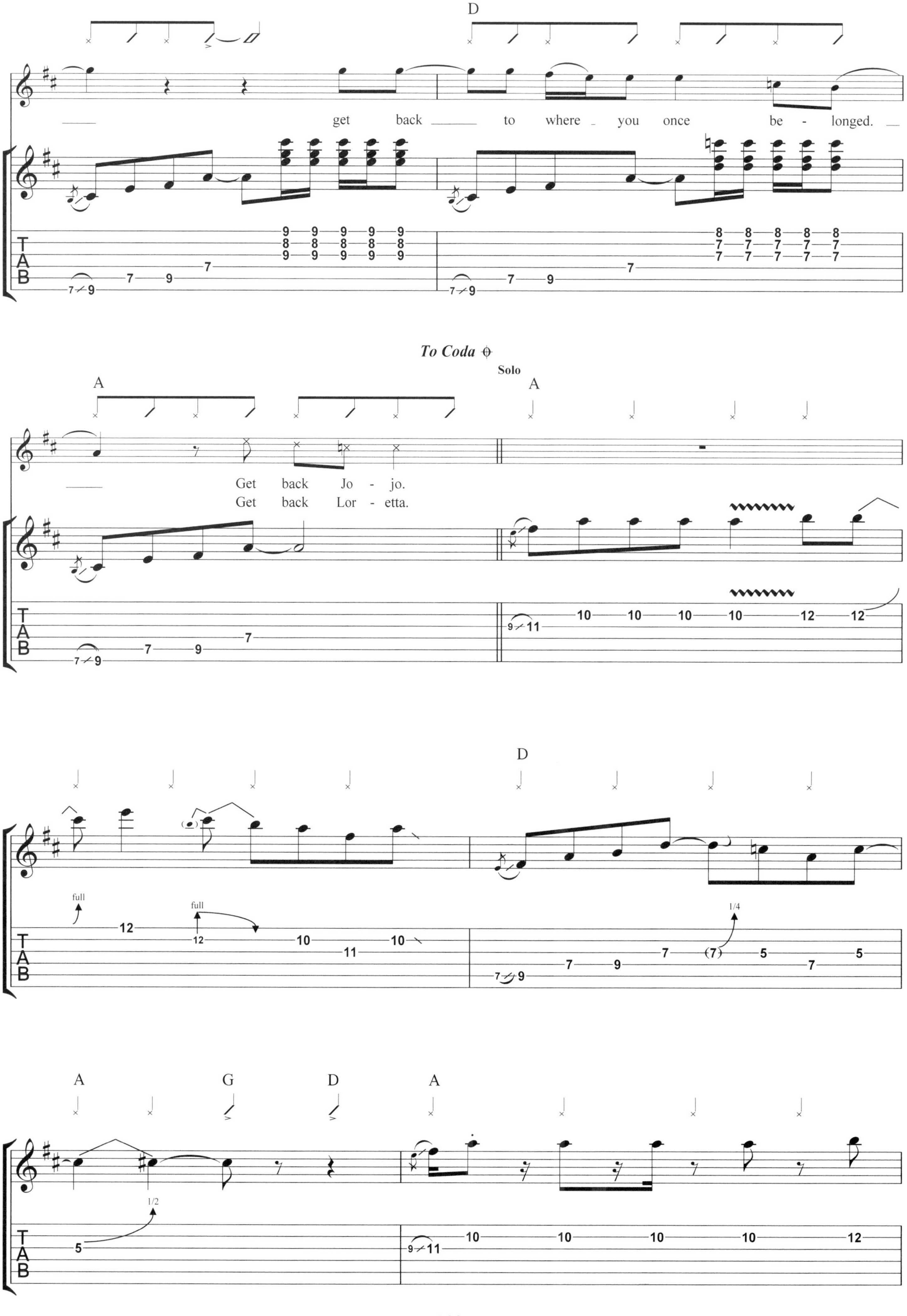
D
get back to where you once be - longed.
To Coda
Solo
A
A
Get back Jo - jo.
Get back Lor - etta.
full
full
D
1/4
A
G
D
A
1/2

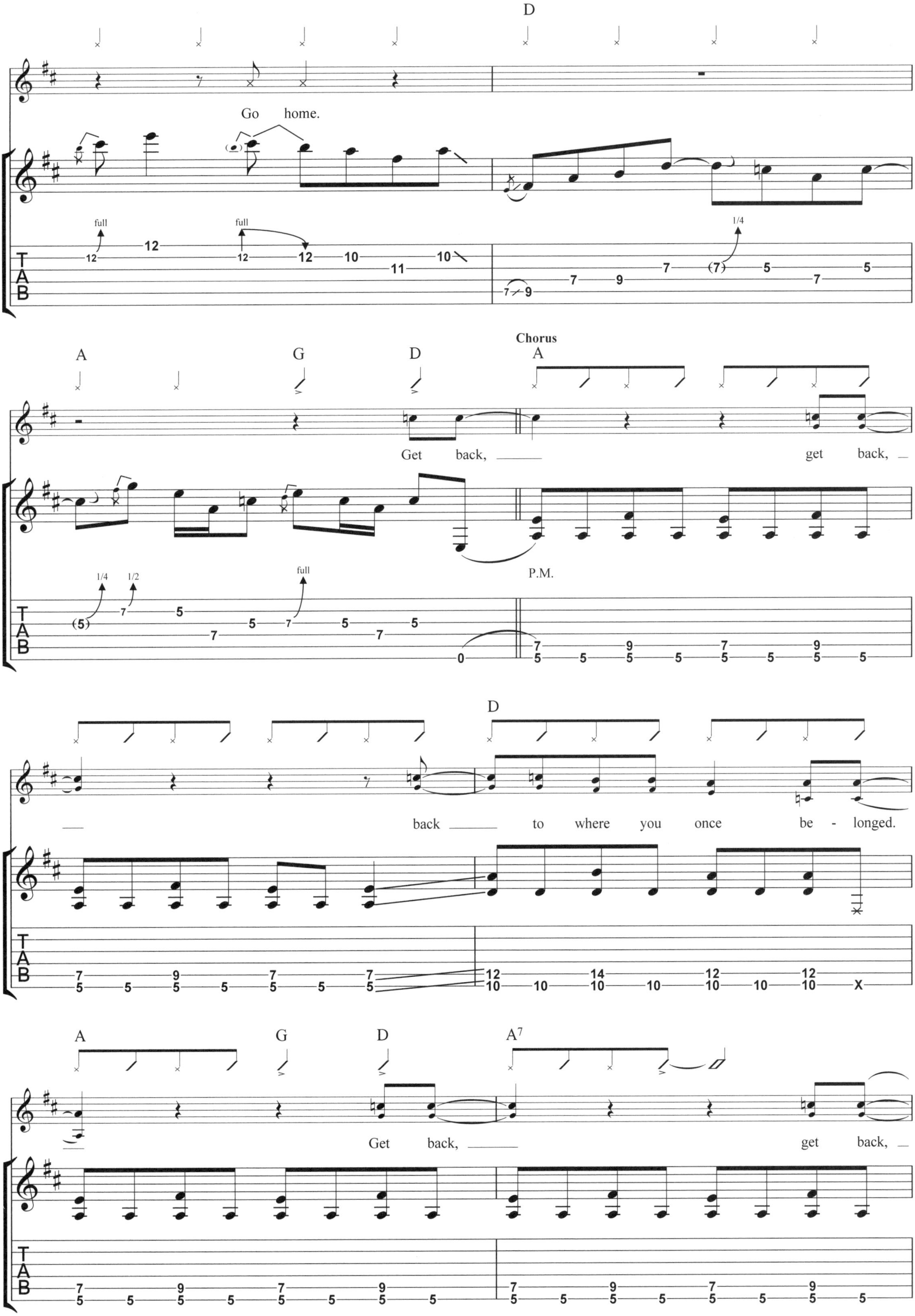
D
Go home.
full
full
1/4
A G D
Chorus
A
Get back, get back,
1/4 1/2 full
P.M.
D
back to where you once be - longed.
A G D A7
Get back, get back,

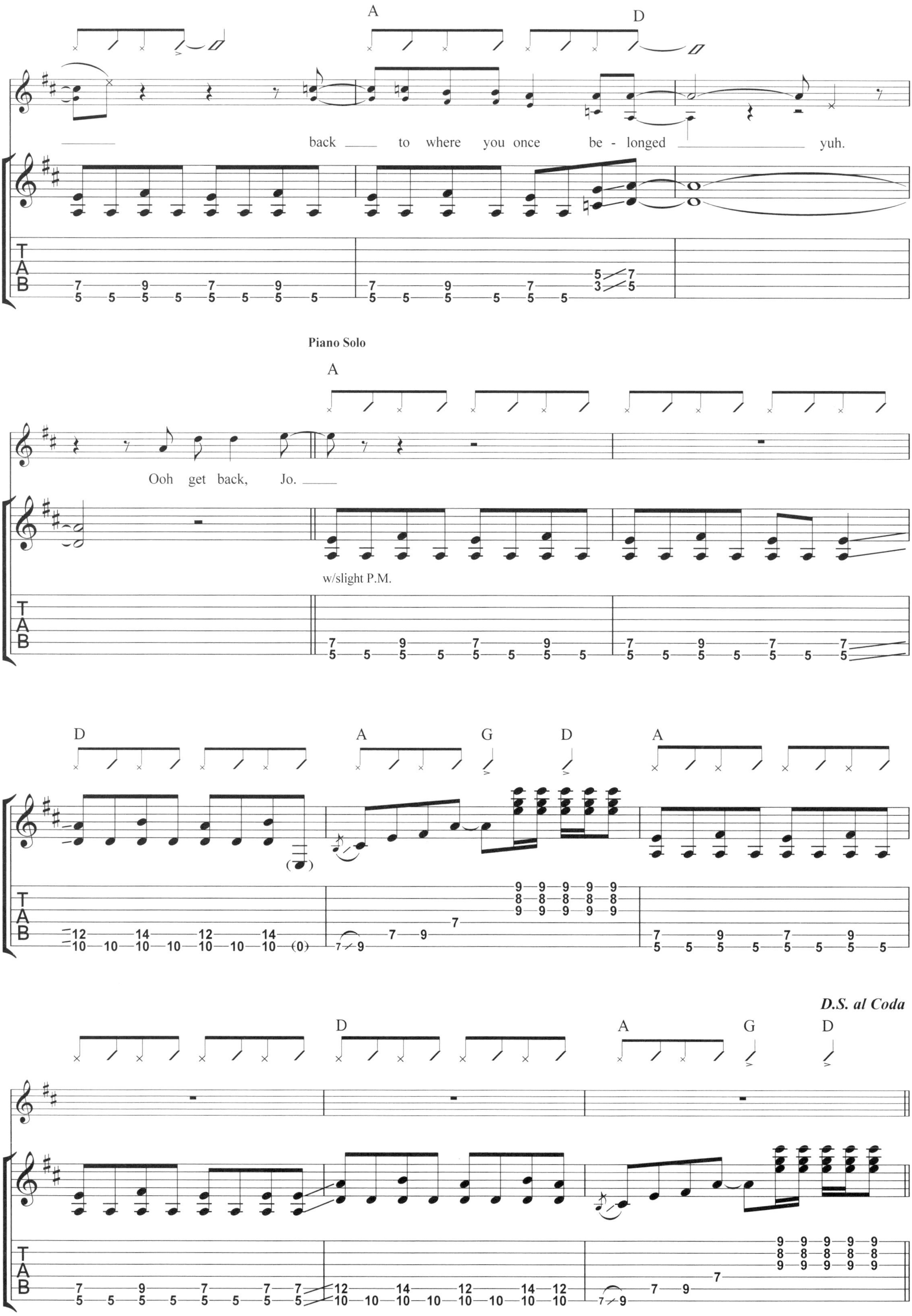
A
D
back to where you once be - longed yuh.
Piano Solo
A
Ooh get back, Jo.
w/slight P.M.
D
A
G
D
A
D.S. al Coda
D
A
G
D

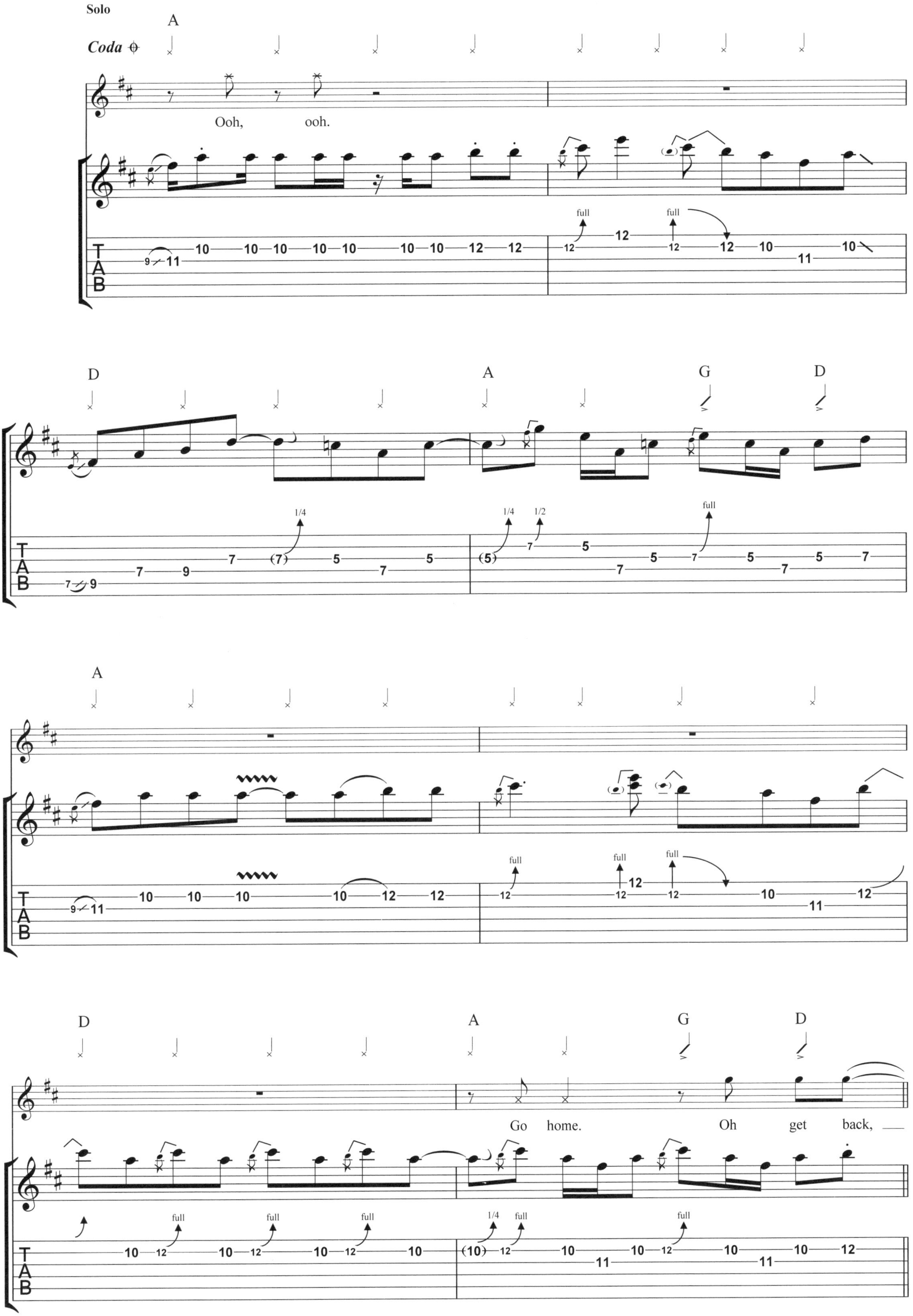
Solo
Coda
A
Ooh, ooh.
full
full
D
A
G
D
1/4
1/4 1/2
full
A
full
full
full
D
A
G
D
Go home. Oh get back,
full
full
full
1/4 full
full

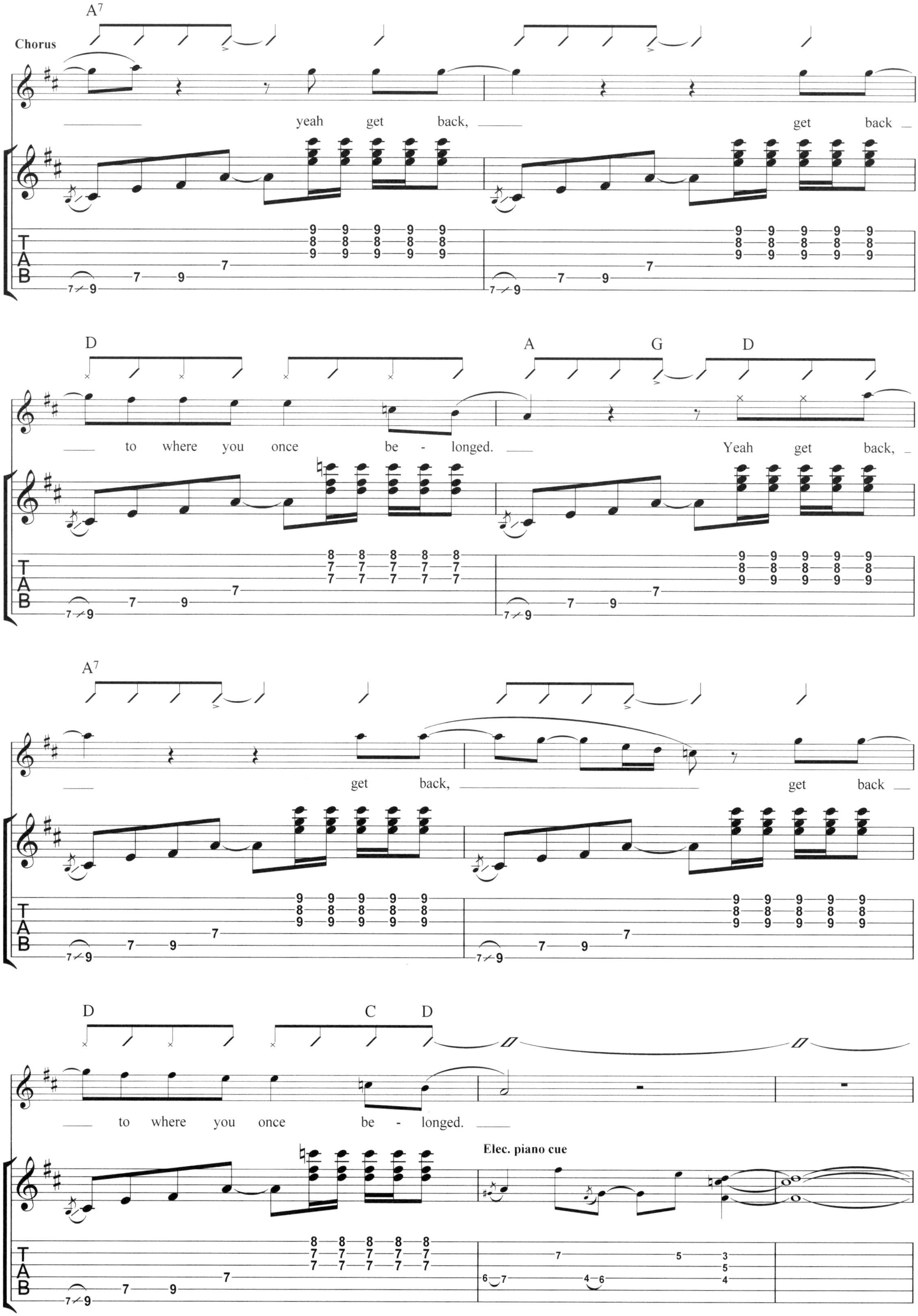
Chorus
A7
yeah get back, get back
D A G D
to where you once be - longed. Yeah get back,
A7
get back, get back
D C D
to where you once be - longed.
Elec. piano cue

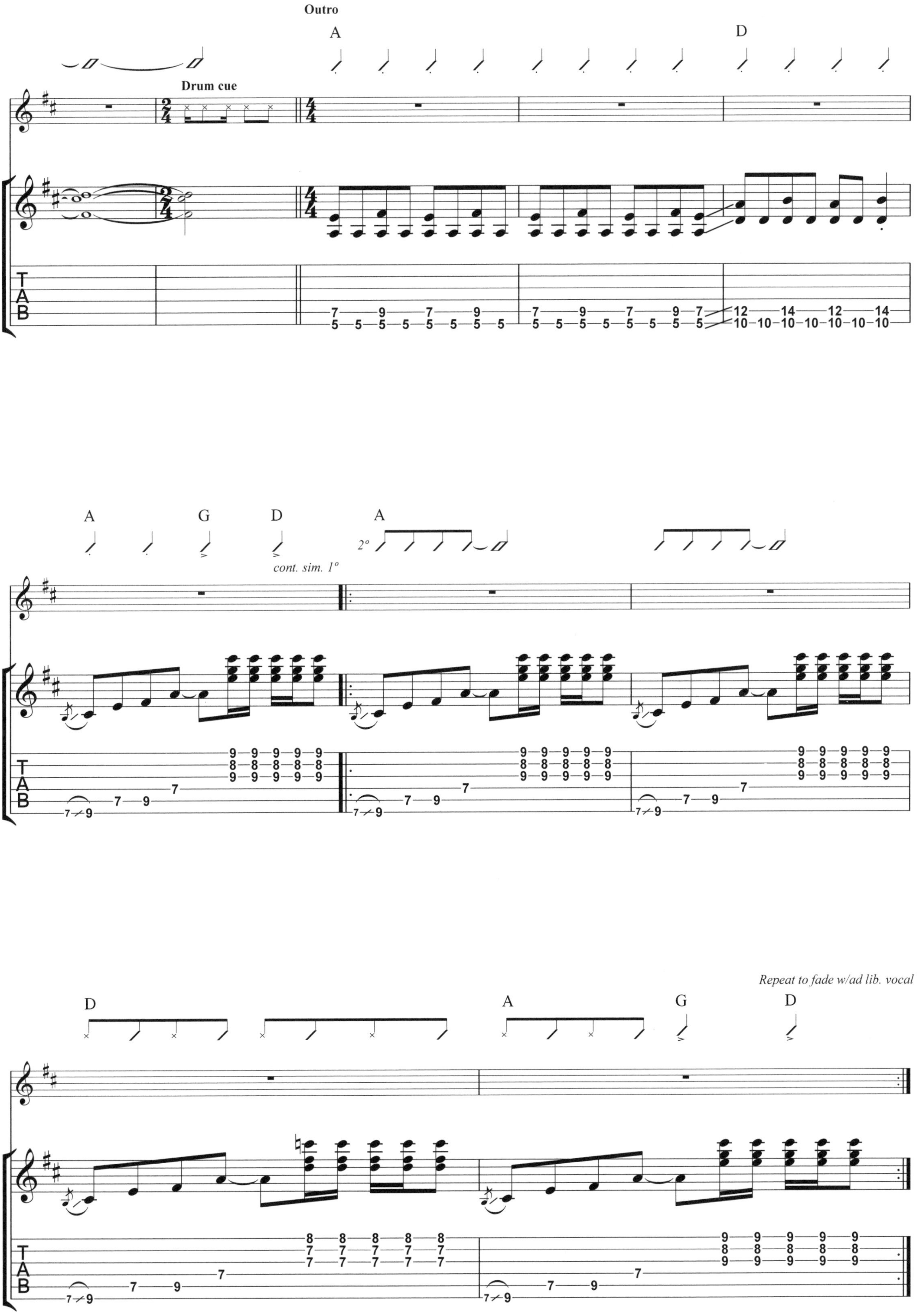
Outro
Drum cue
A
D
A G D
cont. sim. 1º
2º
A
D
A G D
Repeat to fade w/ad lib. vocal

THE BALLAD OF JOHN AND YOKO

Words & Music by John Lennon & Paul McCartney

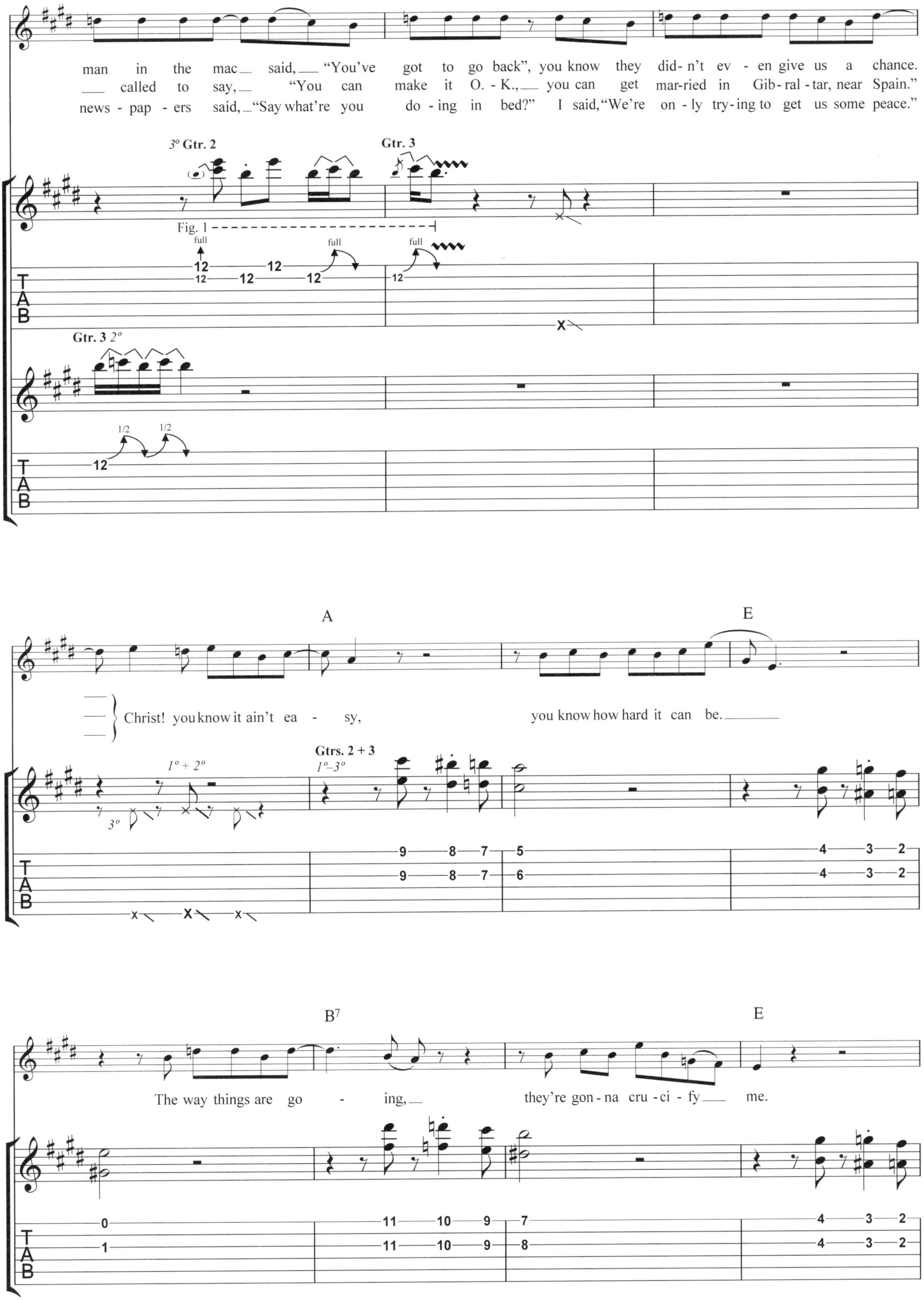
man in the mac said, "You've got to go back", you know they did-n't ev - en give us a chance.
called to say, "You can make it O. - K., you can get mar-ried in Gib - ral - tar, near Spain."
news - pap - ers said, "Say what're you do - ing in bed?" I said, "We're on - ly try-ing to get us some peace."
3º Gtr. 2
Gtr. 3
Fig. 1
full
Gtr. 3 2º
1/2
A
E
Christ! you know it ain't ea - sy, you know how hard it can be.
1º + 2º
3º
Gtrs. 2 + 3
1º–3º
B7
E
The way things are go - ing, they're gon - na cru - ci - fy me.

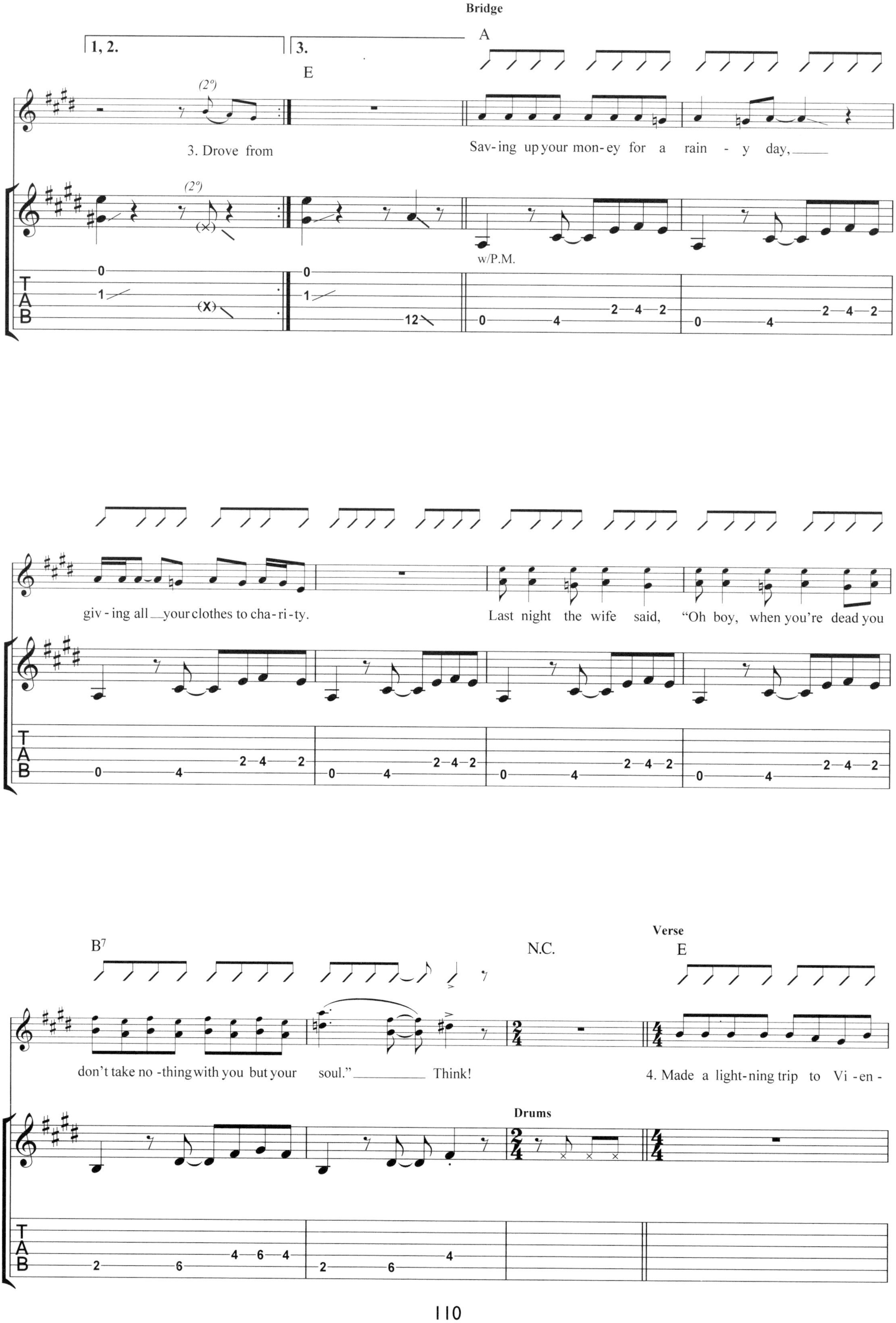
Bridge
1, 2.
3.
E
A
(2º)
3. Drove from
Sav-ing up your mon-ey for a rain - y day,
w/P.M.
giv-ing all your clothes to cha-ri-ty.
Last night the wife said, "Oh boy, when you're dead you
B7
N.C.
Verse
E
don't take no-thing with you but your soul." Think!
4. Made a light-ning trip to Vi-en-
Drums
T
A
B

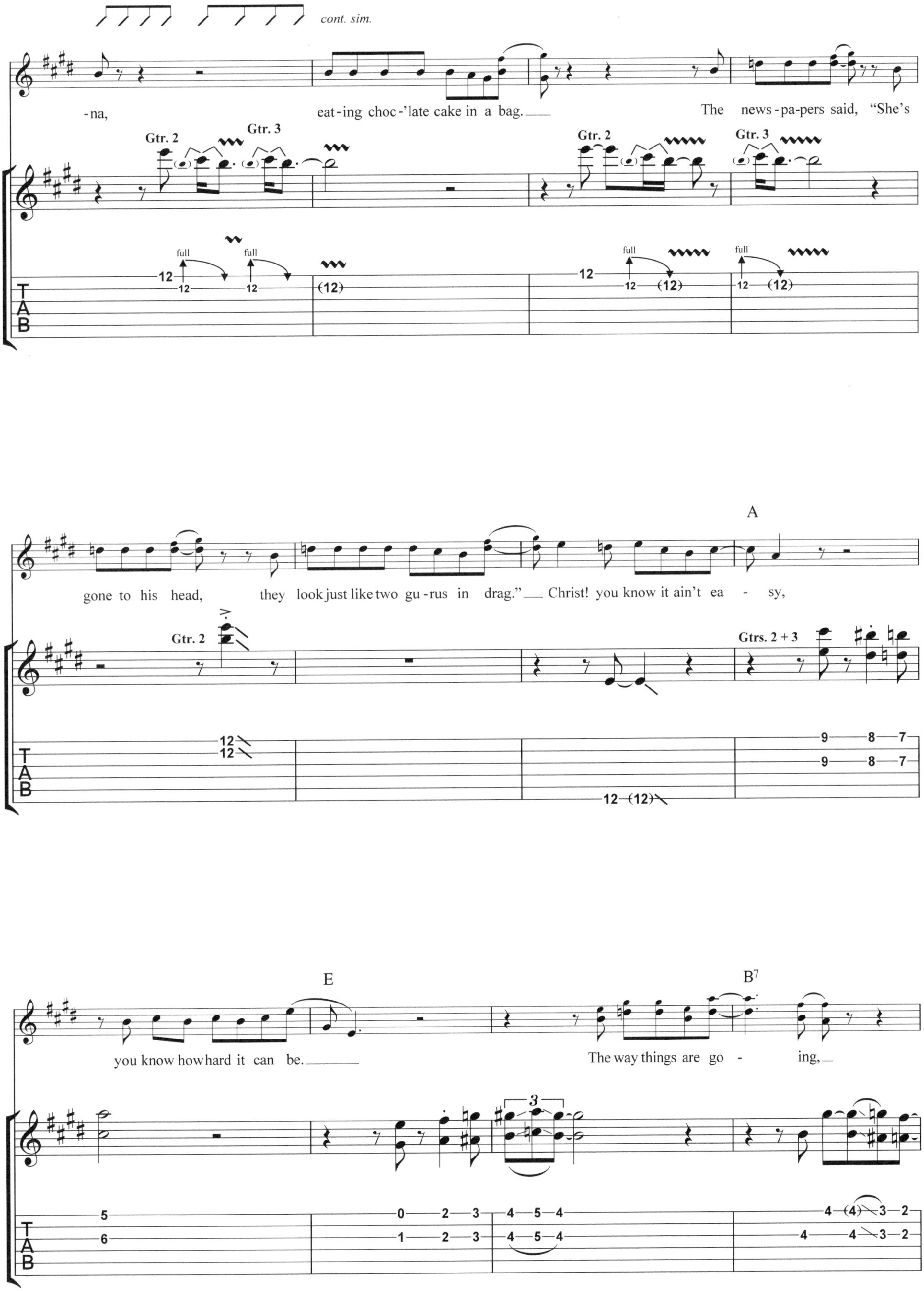
cont. sim.
-na, eat-ing choc-'late cake in a bag. The news-pa-pers said, "She's
Gtr. 2
Gtr. 3
full
full
Gtr. 2
Gtr. 3
full
full
A
gone to his head, they look just like two gu-rus in drag." Christ! you know it ain't ea - sy,
Gtr. 2
Gtrs. 2 + 3
E
B7
you know how hard it can be. The way things are go - ing,

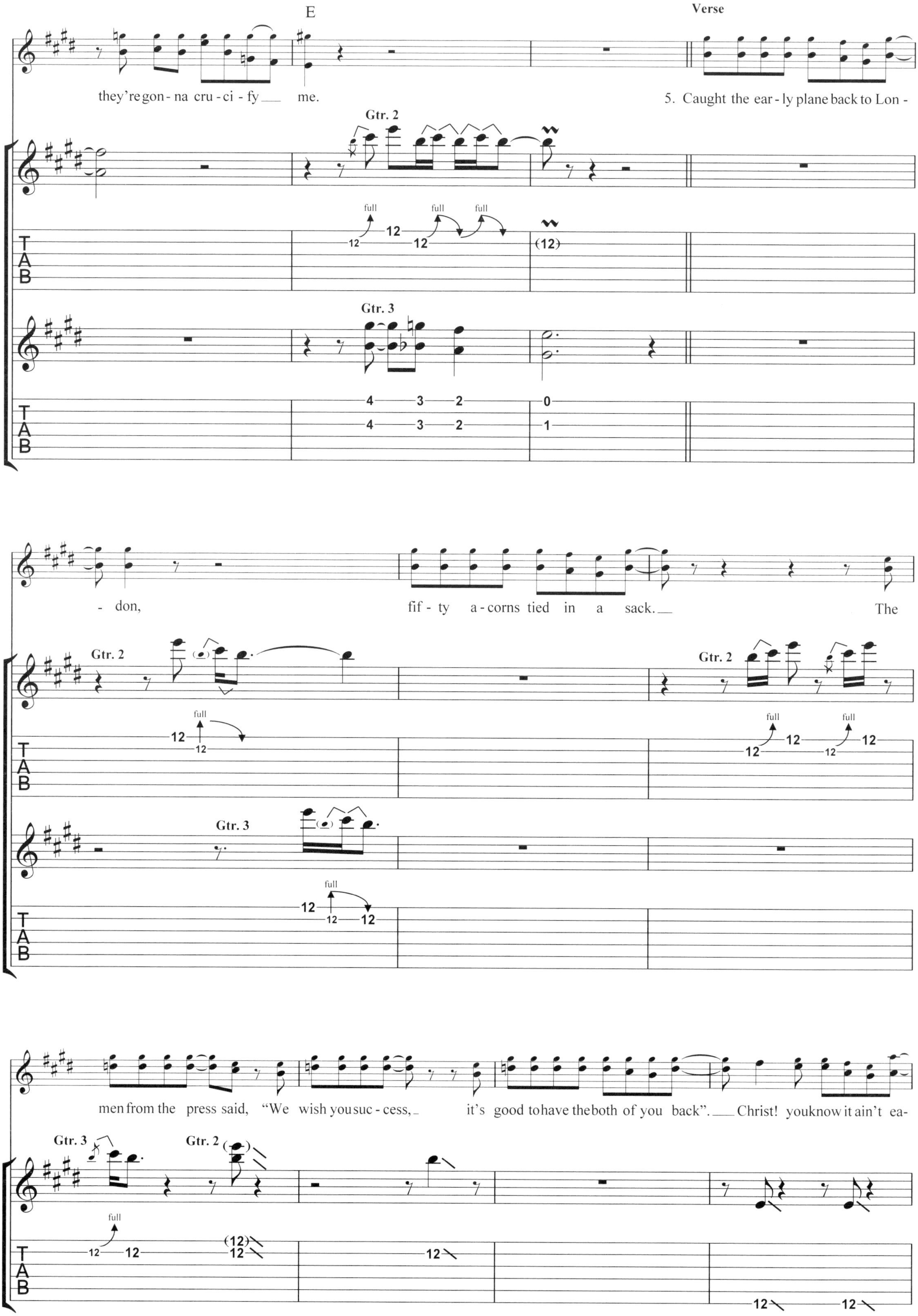
E
Verse
they're gon - na cru - ci - fy ___ me.
5. Caught the ear - ly plane back to Lon -
Gtr. 2
full
Gtr. 3
- don,
fif - ty a - corns tied in a sack. ___
The
men from the press said, "We wish you suc - cess, _
it's good to have the both of you back". ___ Christ! you know it ain't ea-

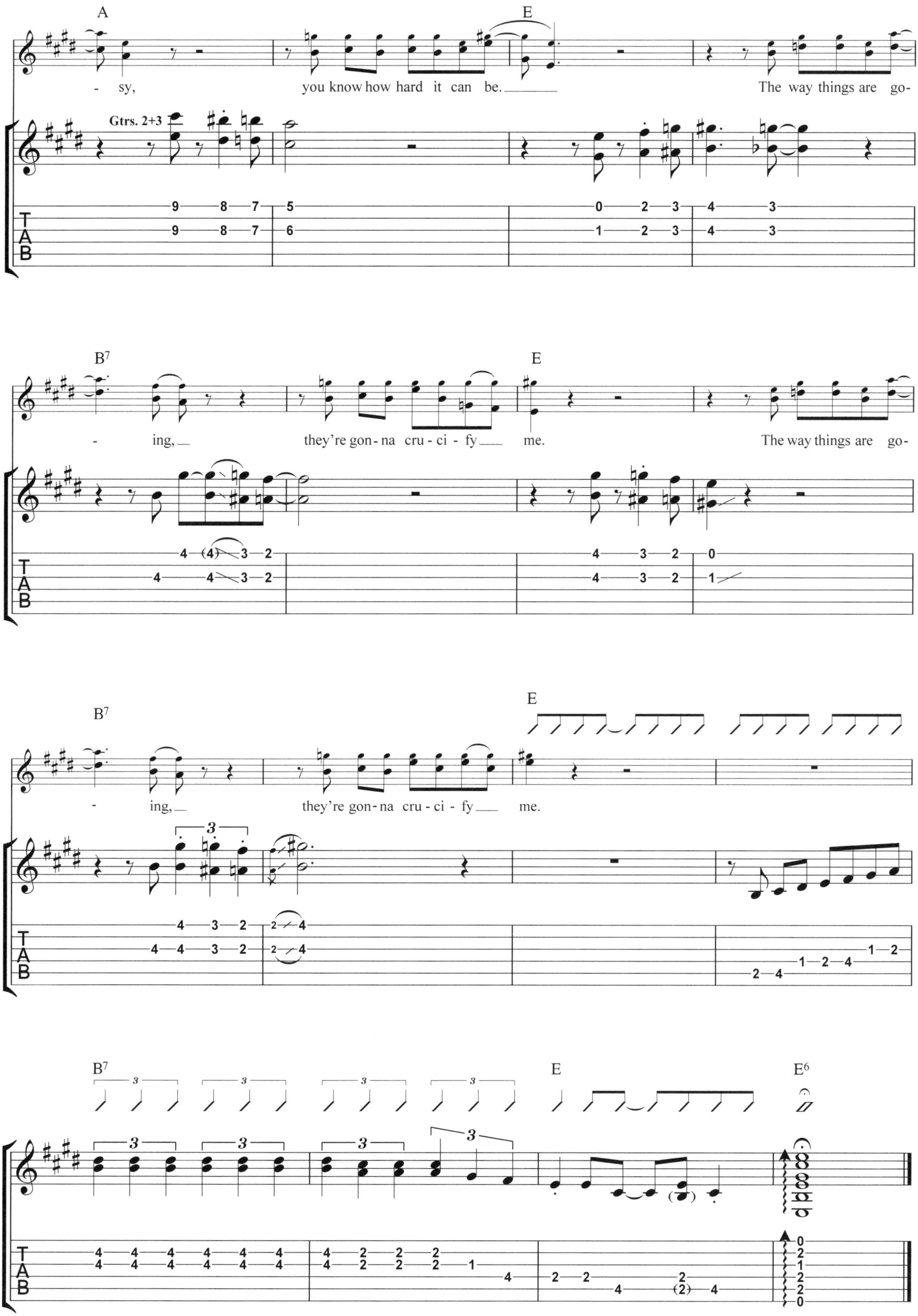
A
E
- sy, you know how hard it can be.
The way things are go-
Gtrs. 2+3
B7
E
- ing, they're gon-na cru-ci-fy me.
The way things are go-
B7
E
- ing, they're gon-na cru-ci-fy me.
B7
E
E6

COME TOGETHER

Words & Music by John Lennon & Paul McCartney

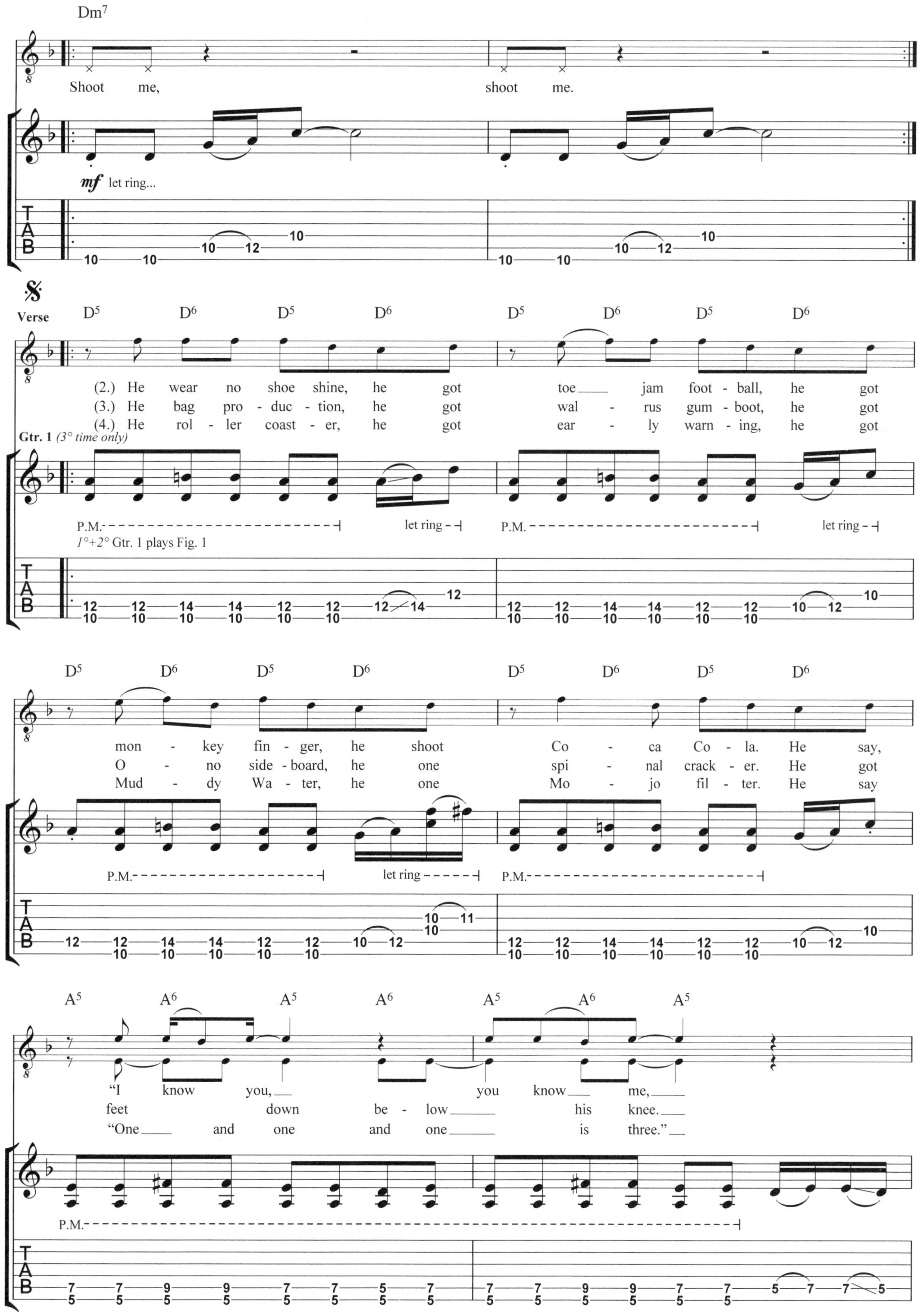
Dm7
Shoot me, shoot me.
mf let ring...
Verse
D5 D6 D5 D6 D5 D6 D5 D6
(2.) He wear no shoe shine, he got toe jam foot - ball, he got
(3.) He bag pro - duc - tion, he got wal - rus gum - boot, he got
(4.) He rol - ler coast - er, he got ear - ly warn - ing, he got
Gtr. 1 (3° time only)
P.M.
let ring
1°+2° Gtr. 1 plays Fig. 1
D5 D6 D5 D6 D5 D6 D5 D6
mon - key fin - ger, he shoot Co - ca Co - la. He say,
O - no side - board, he one spi - nal crack - er. He got
Mud - dy Wa - ter, he one Mo - jo fil - ter. He say
A5 A6 A5 A6 A5 A6 A5
"I know you, you know me,
feet down be - low his knee.
"One and one and one is three."
P.M.

G5
One thing I can tell you is you got to be free."
Hold you in his arm - chair, you can feel his dis - ease.
Got to be good look - in' 'cause he's so hard to see.
Come to - geth -
switch to bridge pickup
Chorus
B5 A6* G5 A5 Dm7
To Coda
- er, right now, ov - er me.
to neck pickup
let ring...
1.
2.
Shoot me, shoot me, shoot me. Shoot me, right!
Interlude
D5 D6 D5 D6 D5 D6 D5 D6 D5 D6 D5 D6 D5 D6 D5 D6
Here it comes.

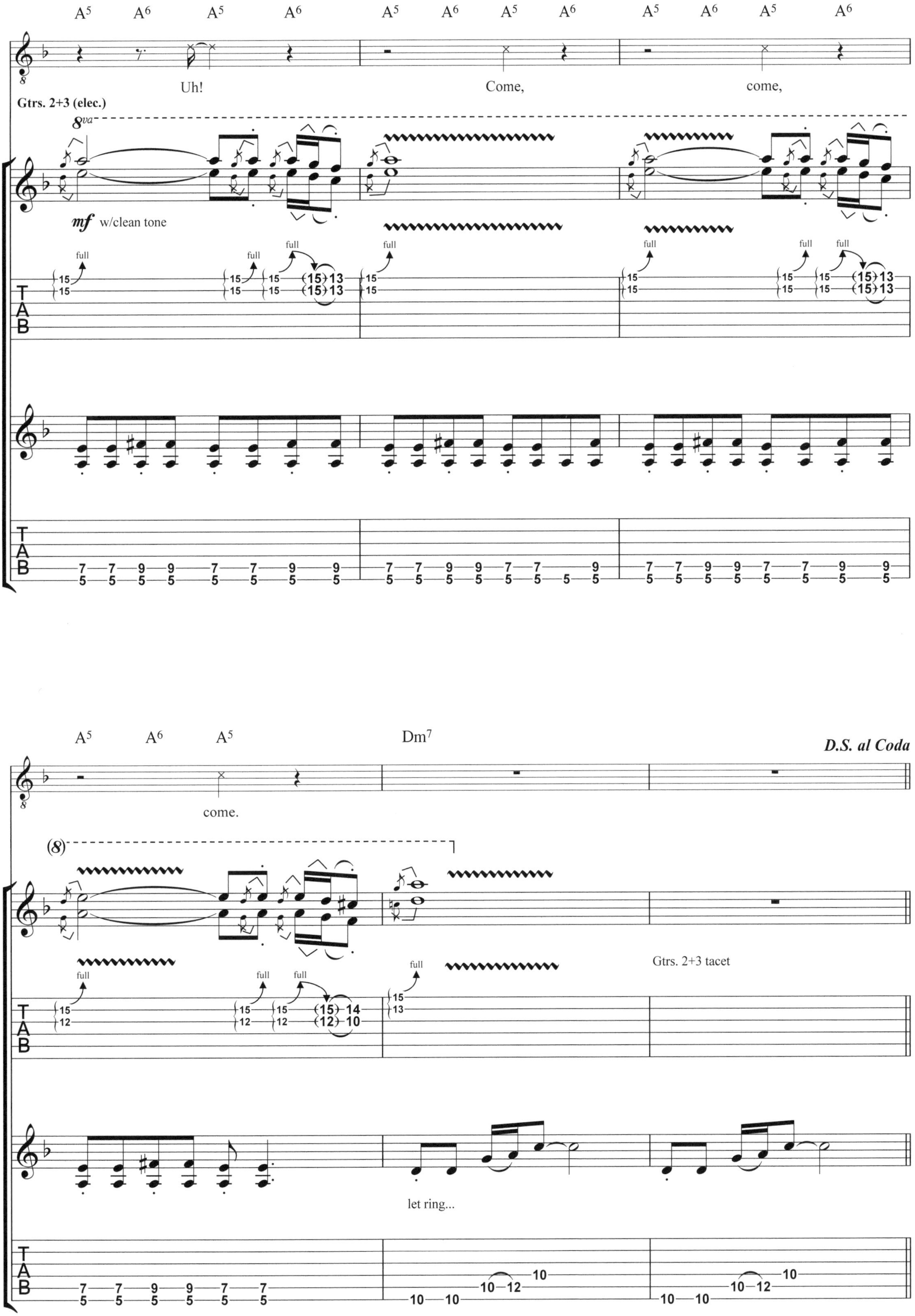
A5 A6 A5 A6 A5 A6 A5 A6 A5 A6 A5 A6
Uh!
Come,
come,
Gtrs. 2+3 (elec.)
8va
mf w/clean tone
full
A5 A6 A5
Dm7
D.S. al Coda
come.
(8)
Gtrs. 2+3 tacet
let ring...

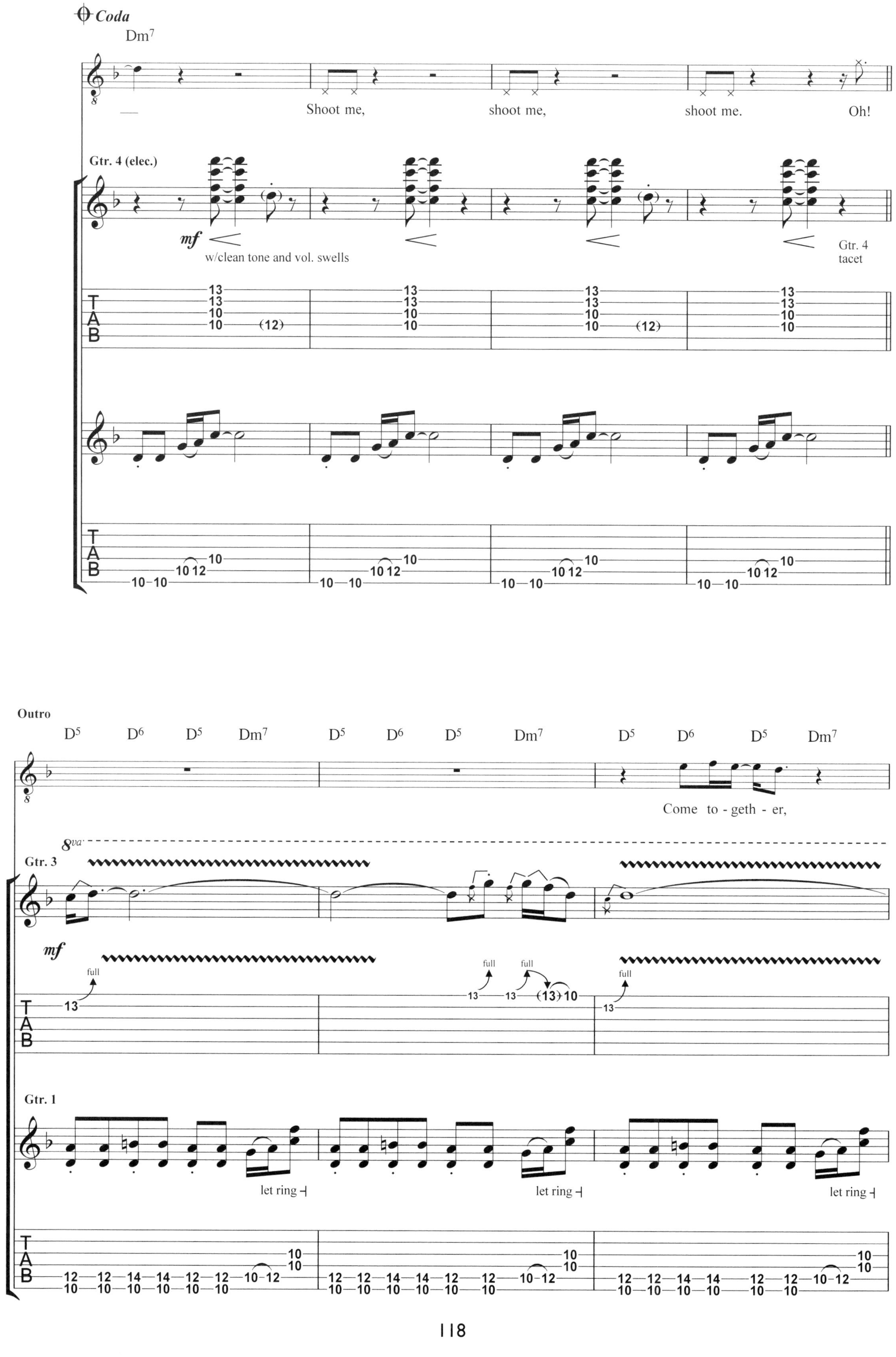
Coda
Dm7
Shoot me,
shoot me,
shoot me.
Oh!
Gtr. 4 (elec.)
mf
w/clean tone and vol. swells
Gtr. 4 tacet
Outro
D5 D6 D5 Dm7 D5 D6 D5 Dm7 D5 D6 D5 Dm7
Come to - geth - er,
8va
Gtr. 3
mf
full
Gtr. 1
let ring

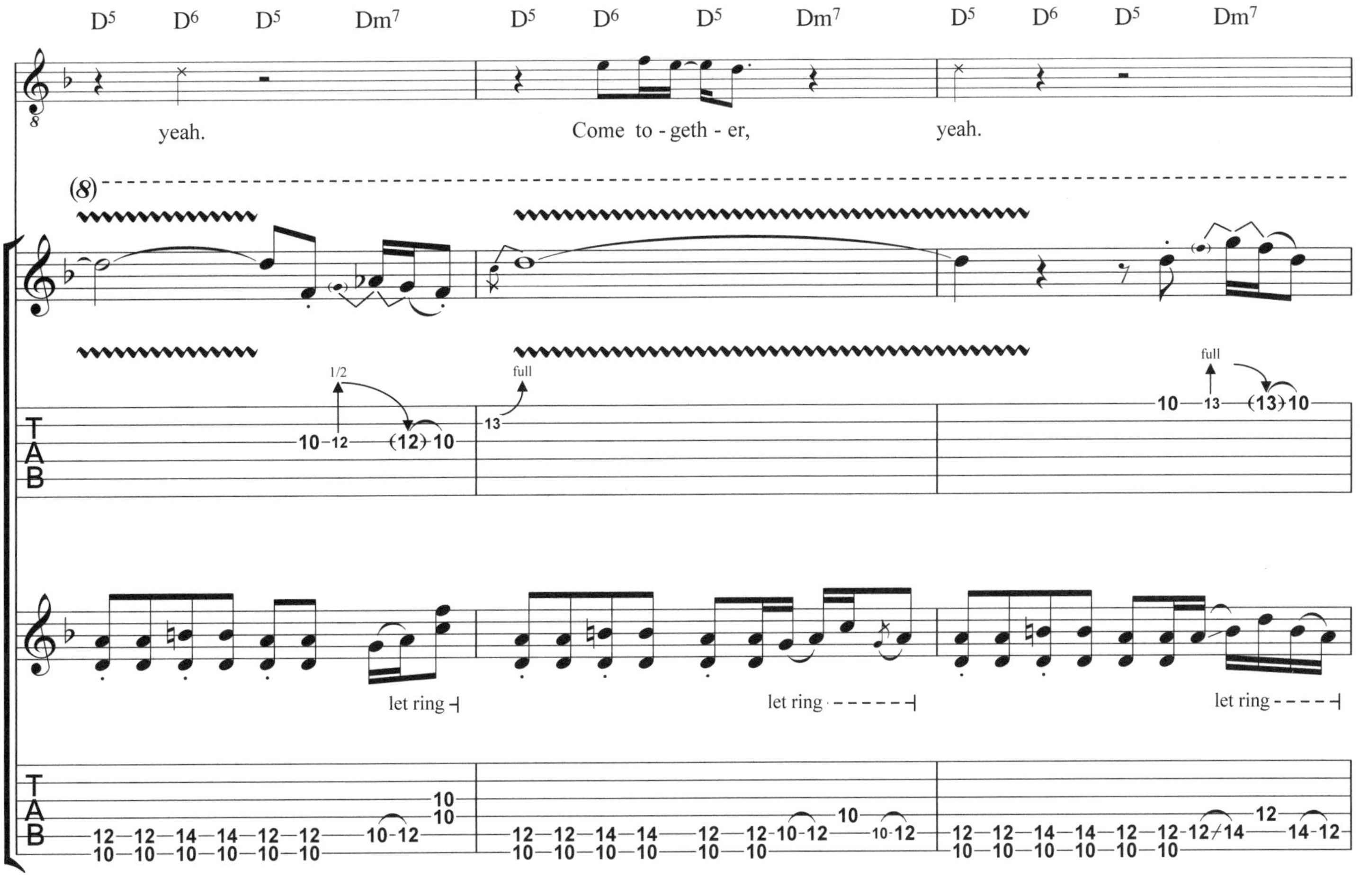
D5 D6 D5 Dm7 D5 D6 D5 Dm7 D5 D6 D5 Dm7
yeah.
Come to-geth-er,
yeah.
(8)
1/2
full
full
let ring
let ring
let ring

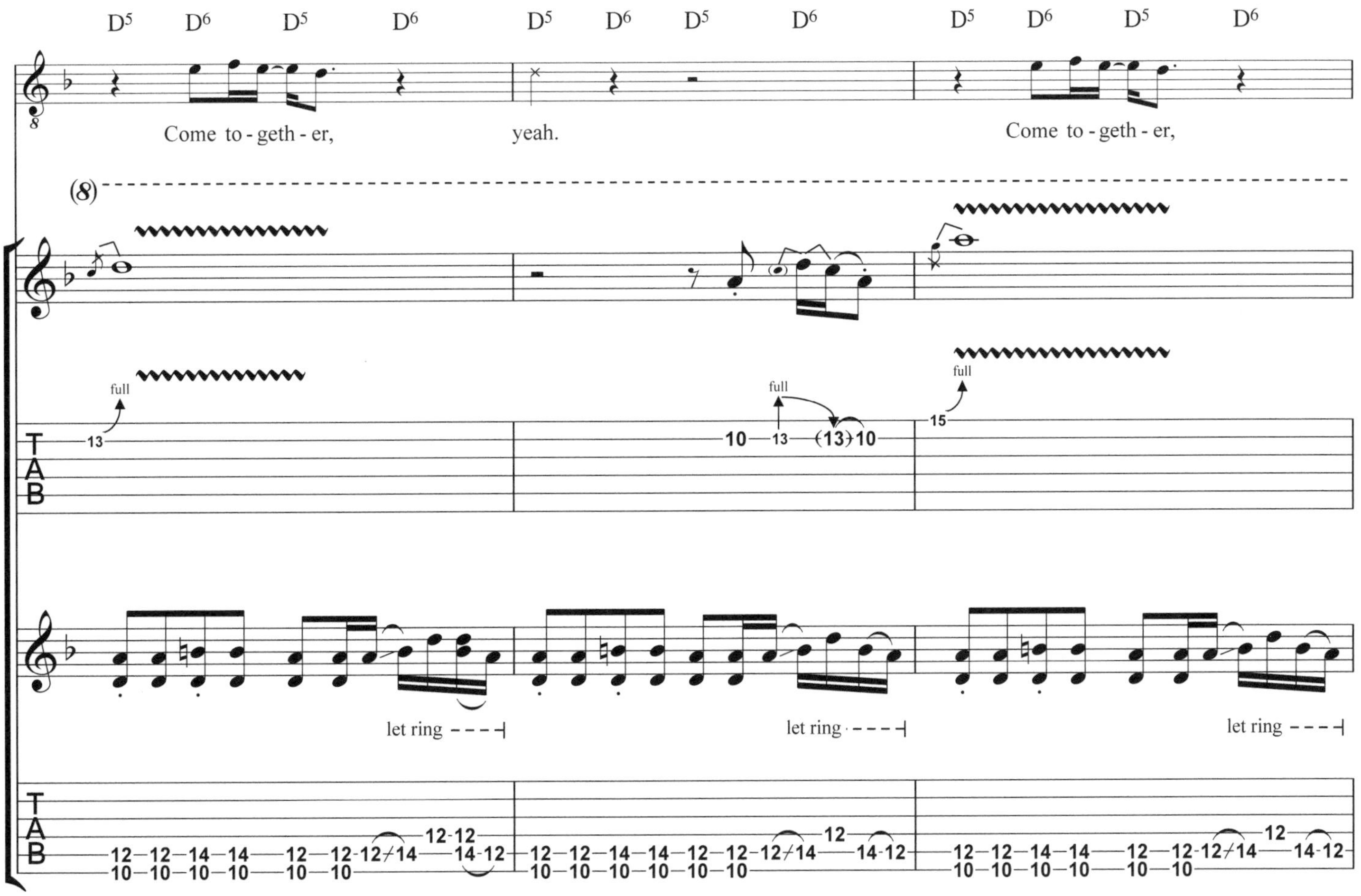
D5 D6 D5 D6 D5 D6 D5 D6 D5 D6 D5 D6
Come to-geth-er,
yeah.
Come to-geth-er,
(8)
full
full
full
let ring
let ring
let ring

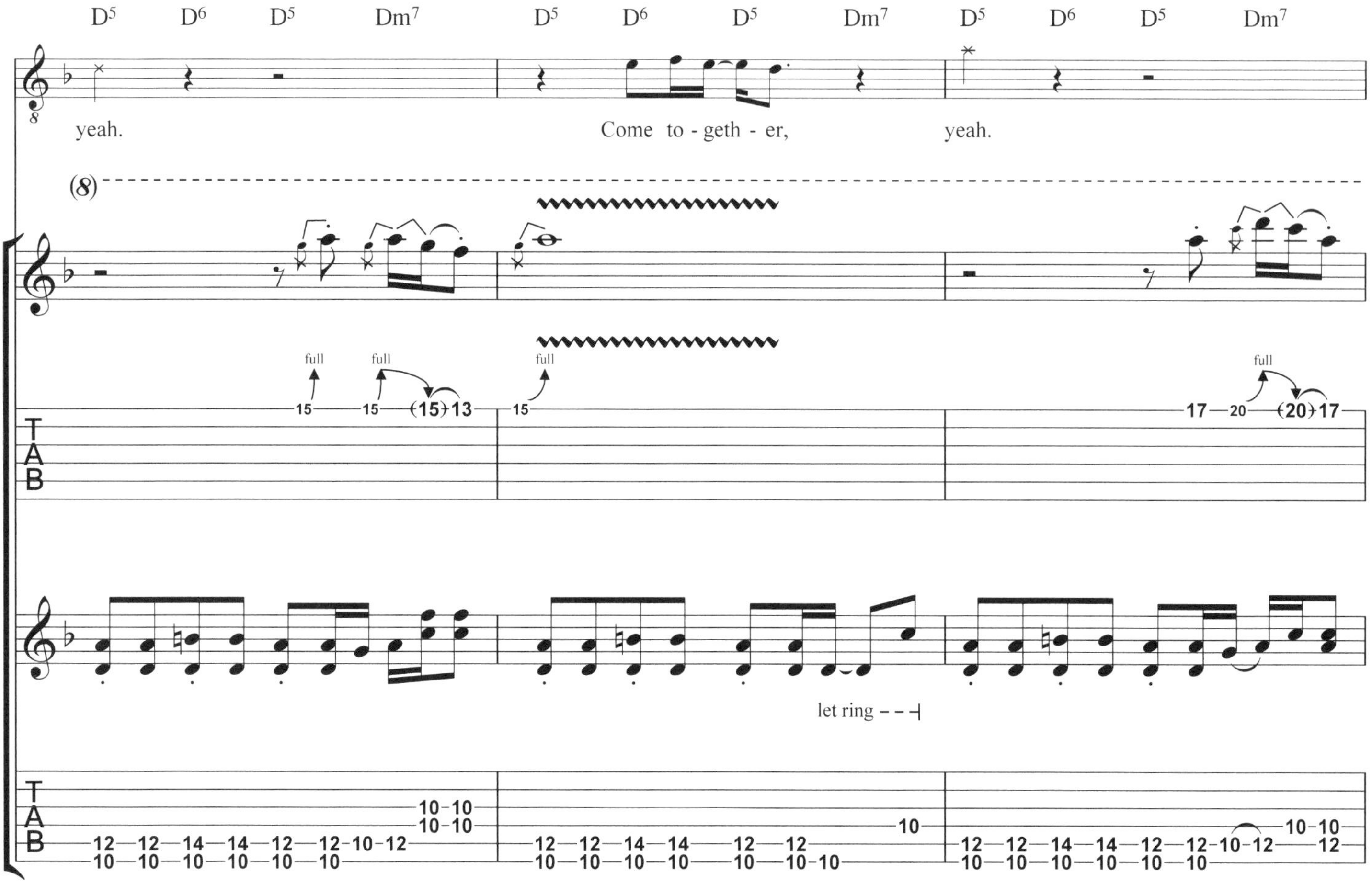
D5 D6 D5 Dm7 D5 D6 D5 Dm7 D5 D6 D5 Dm7
yeah.
Come to - geth - er,
yeah.
(8)
full
full
full
full
let ring
T
A
B

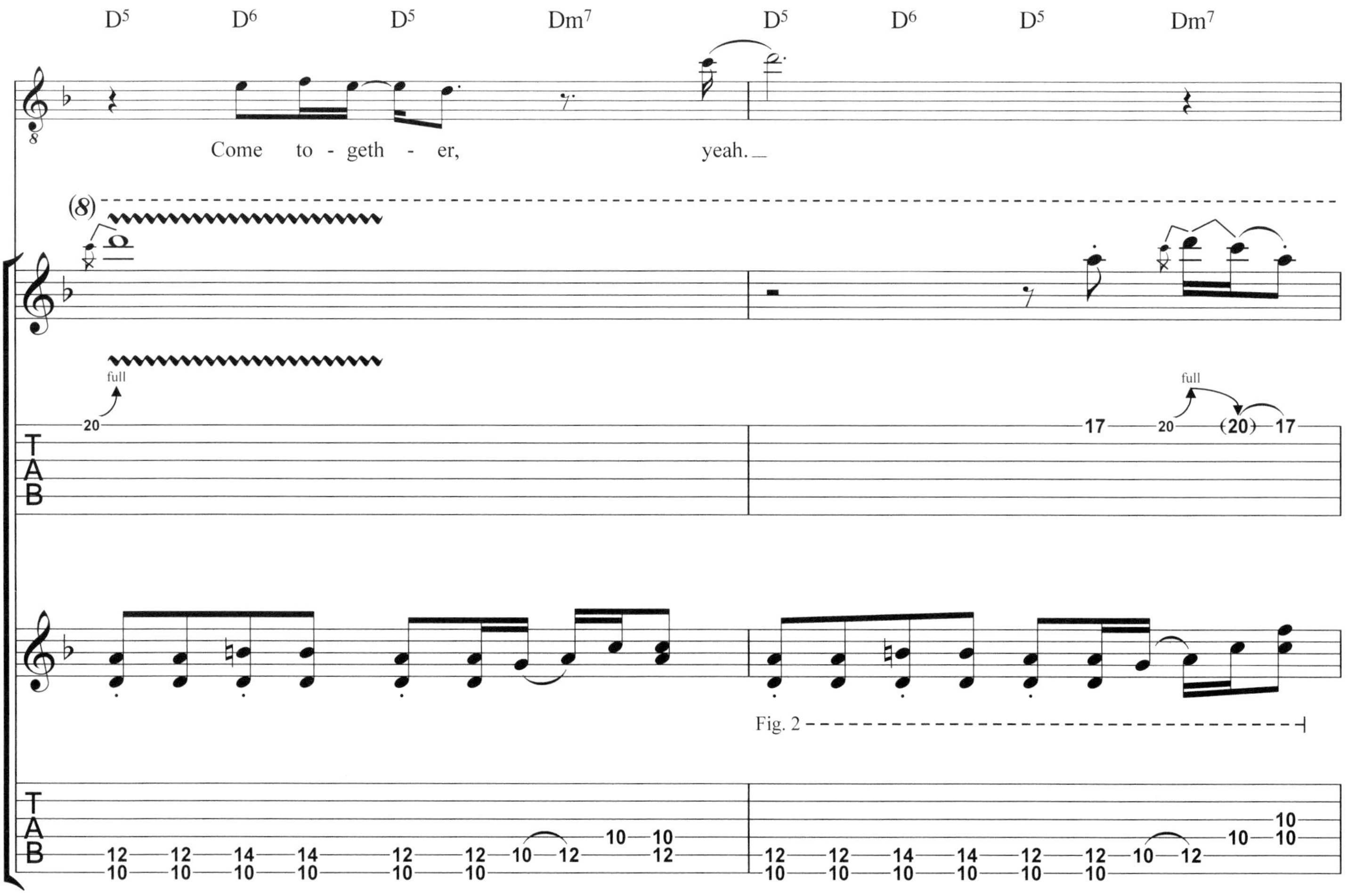
D5 D6 D5 Dm7 D5 D6 D5 Dm7
Come to - geth - er,
yeah.
(8)
full
full
Fig. 2
T
A
B

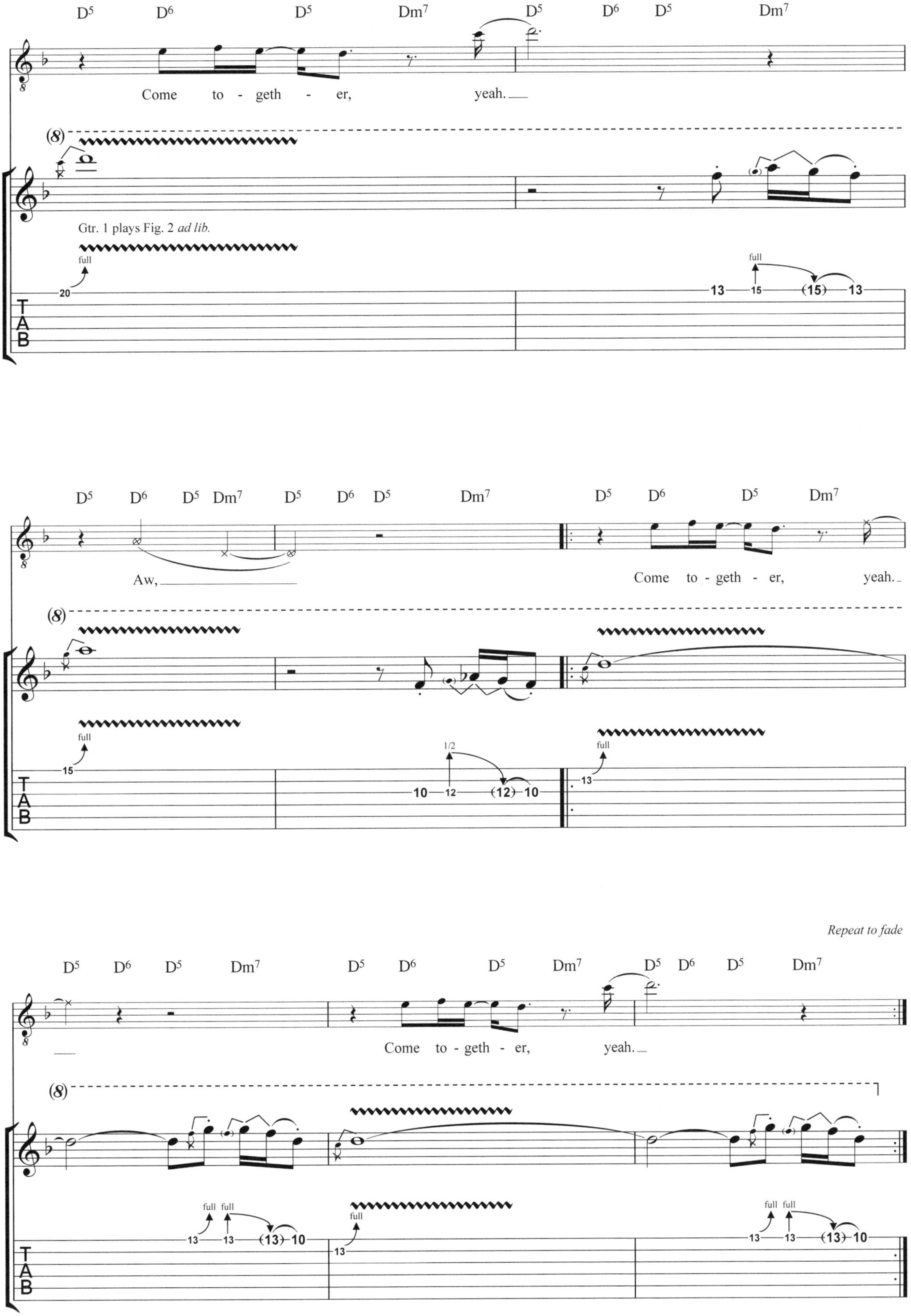
D5 D6 D5 Dm7 D5 D6 D5 Dm7
Come to - geth - er, yeah.
Gtr. 1 plays Fig. 2 ad lib.
full
D5 D6 D5 Dm7 D5 D6 D5 Dm7 D5 D6 D5 Dm7
Aw,
Come to - geth - er, yeah.
Repeat to fade
D5 D6 D5 Dm7 D5 D6 D5 Dm7 D5 D6 D5 Dm7
Come to - geth - er, yeah.
TAB

LET IT BE

Words & Music by John Lennon & Paul McCartney

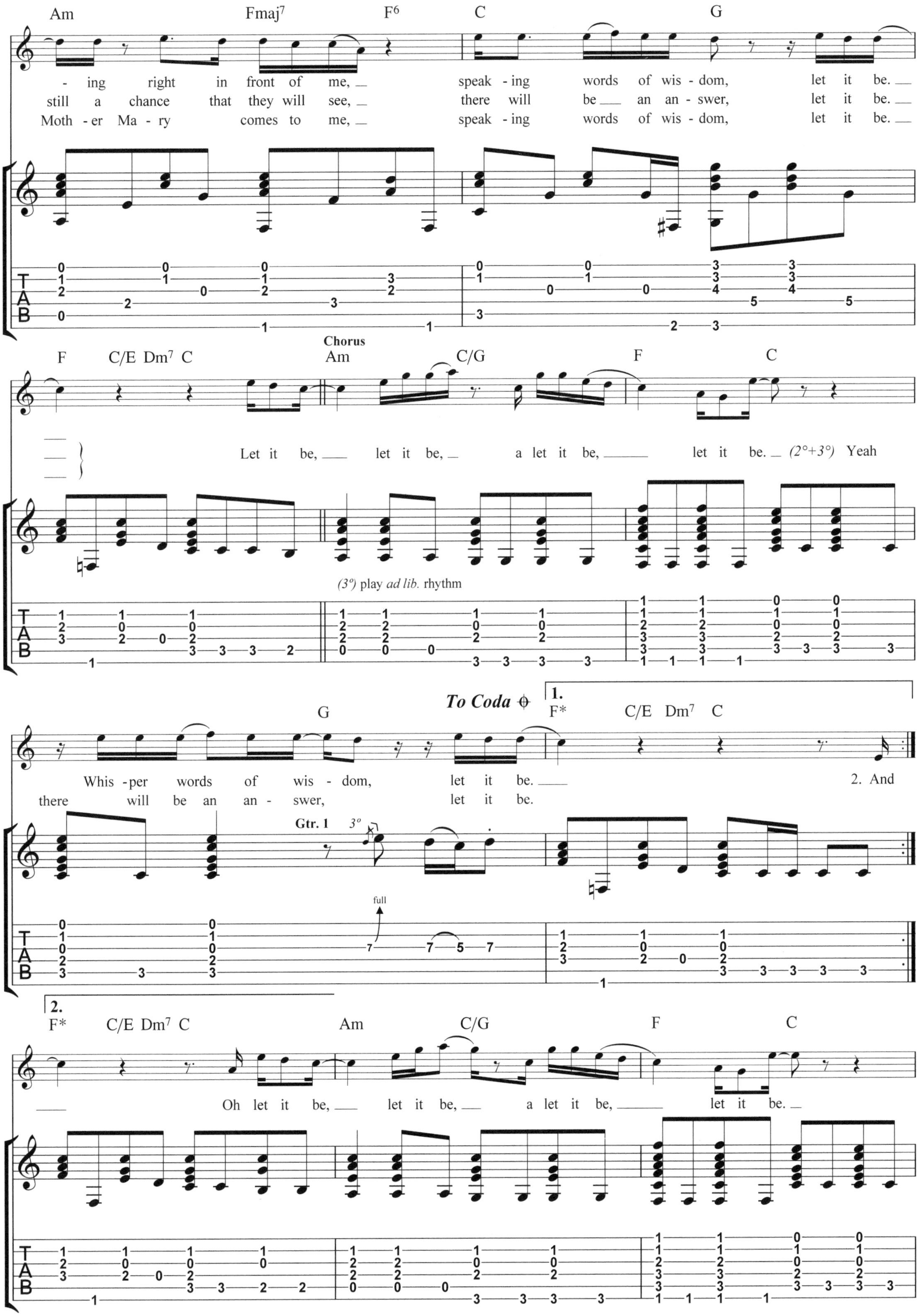
Am Fmaj7 F6 C G
- ing right in front of me, speak - ing words of wis - dom, let it be.
still a chance that they will see, there will be an an - swer, let it be.
Moth - er Ma - ry comes to me, speak - ing words of wis - dom, let it be.
Chorus
F C/E Dm7 C Am C/G F C
Let it be, let it be, a let it be, let it be. (2°+3°) Yeah
(3°) play ad lib. rhythm
To Coda
1.
G F* C/E Dm7 C
Whis - per words of wis - dom, let it be. 2. And
there will be an an - swer, let it be.
Gtr. 1 3°
full
2.
F* C/E Dm7 C Am C/G F C
Oh let it be, let it be, a let it be, let it be.

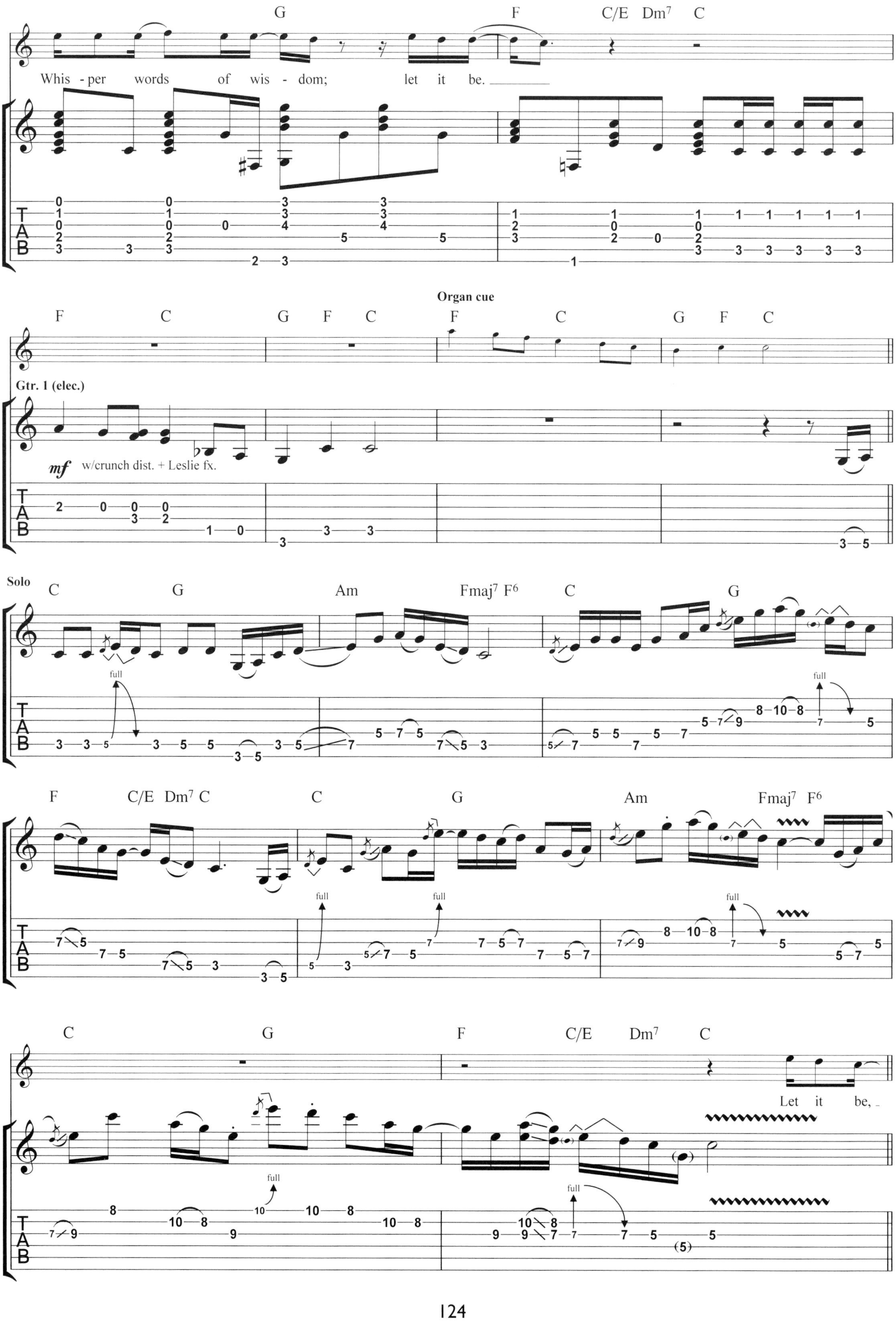
G F C/E Dm7 C
Whis - per words of wis - dom; let it be.
Organ cue
F C G F C F C G F C
Gtr. 1 (elec.)
mf w/crunch dist. + Leslie fx.
Solo
C G Am Fmaj7 F6 C G
full
F C/E Dm7 C C G Am Fmaj7 F6
C G F C/E Dm7 C
Let it be,

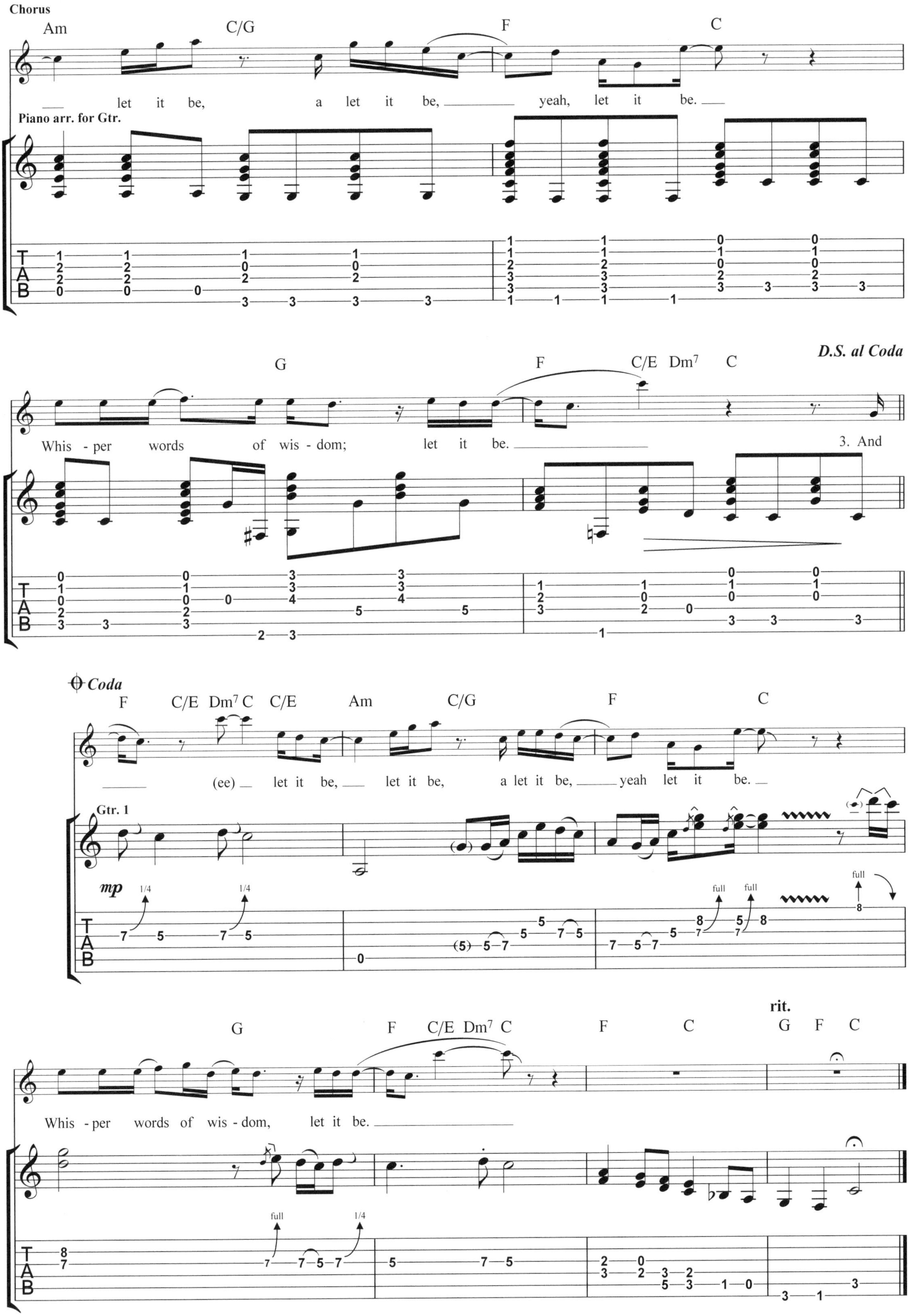
Chorus
Am C/G F C
let it be, a let it be, yeah, let it be.
Piano arr. for Gtr.
G F C/E Dm7 C
D.S. al Coda
Whis - per words of wis - dom; let it be.
3. And
Coda
F C/E Dm7 C C/E Am C/G F C
(ee) let it be, let it be, a let it be, yeah let it be.
Gtr. 1
mp
1/4
full
G F C/E Dm7 C F C G F C
rit.
Whis - per words of wis - dom, let it be.

THE LONG AND WINDING ROAD

Words & Music by John Lennon & Paul McCartney

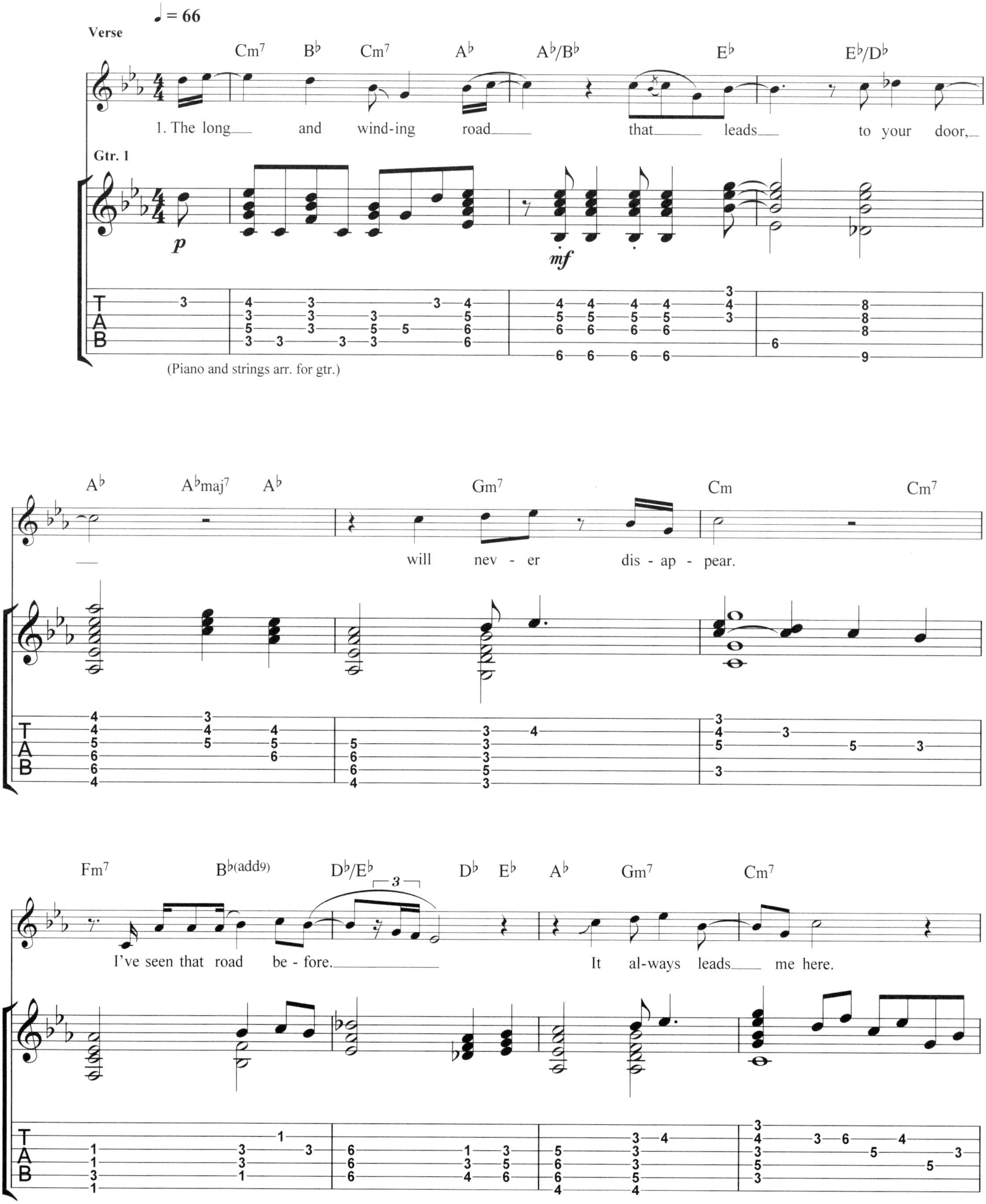

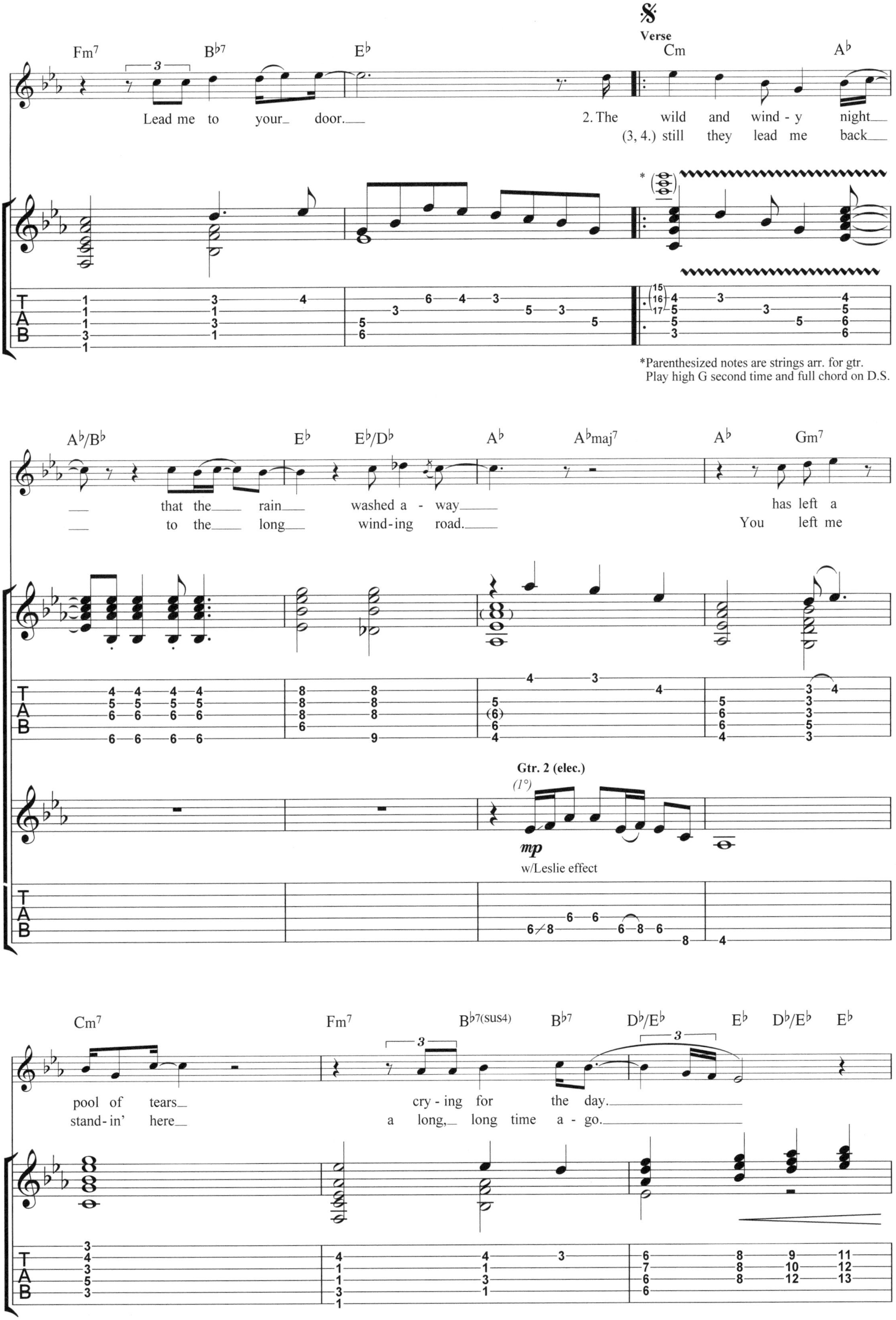

*Parenthesized notes are strings arr. for gtr.
Play high G second time and full chord on D.S.

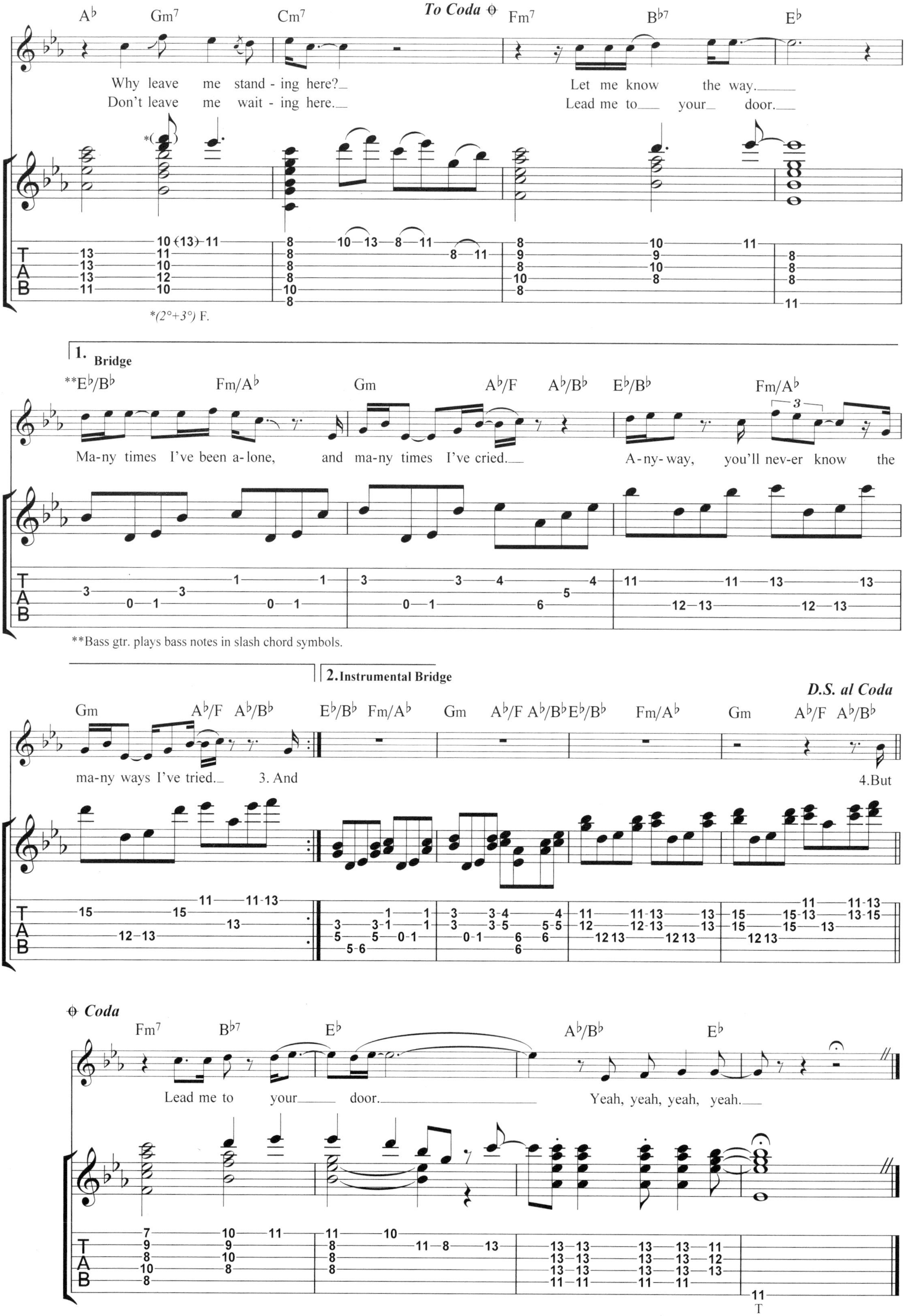

1 2 3 4 5 6 7 8 9
7/12(183937)